NEW ENGLAND'S
RARE, THREATENED, AND ENDANGERED PLANTS

by
Garrett E. Crow
University of New Hampshire

in collaboration with the
New England Botanical Club Endangered Species Committee
W. D. Countryman, chairman
G. E. Crow, vice-chairman
G. L. Church
L. M. Eastman
C. B. Hellquist
L. J. Mehrhoff

illustrated by
Tess Feltes

prepared for the
United States Department of the Interior
Fish and Wildlife Service
Northeast Region

in cooperation with the
New Hampshire Agricultural Experiment Station
University of New Hampshire

June 1982

For sale by the Superintendent of Documents, U.S. Government Printing Office, Washington, D.C. 20402
Stock No. 024-010-00605-6

FOREWORD

One's concern for endangered and threatened species is a value judgment that each of us must independently seek and refine. It is often a personal emotion tempered by the knowledge, understanding and appreciation of the natural world in which we live. Although some species inherently have more emotional appeal, it matters little among bird, mammal, fish, invertebrate or plant for there is a commonality in being endangered. Shopping malls, housing projects and highways do not discriminate among life forms.

Plants are the foundation of human existence, and concerns voiced on behalf of those that are endangered and threatened have particular significance. Scientists caution that plants have the potential to produce new sources of food, chemicals, energy and medicine for the world's ever increasing population. The concern for endangered and threatened species, however, must be more than a scientific assessment of a species' utilitarian value or a moral expression on all creatures' basic right to exist. The Grey Whale, the Bald Eagle and the Robbins' Cinquefoil perhaps symbolize the ever elusive quality of life in our existence; but there is much more. Endangered and threatened species possess the unique ability to force us to ponder our relationship with the natural world we share and make us cognizant of the intricacy and fragility of that relationship. This quality could be their single, greatest value if we endeavor to cherish, to conserve, to understand.

Richard W. Dyer

Richard W. Dyer
June 1982

ACKNOWLEDGEMENTS

The collaborative efforts of Bill Countryman, George Church, Les Eastman, Barre Hellquist, and Les Mehrhoff, fellow members of the New England Botanical Club's Endangered Species Committee, were essential to the preparation of this report. Likewise, the continued interest, support, and encouragement of Dick Dyer made this project possible. To them I extend my deepest gratitude. A special word of thanks goes to Tess Feltes for her patience and dedication in preparing the excellent botanical illustrations and Debra Blauvelt for report layout and design.

The assistance of Frankie Brackley in preparing the maps and Lynn Bohs in gathering background literature was especially appreciated. Ernie Schuyler's advice on *Scirpus* and Bruce Sorrie's information on rare plants of southeastern Massachusetts is gratefully acknowledged. Several photographs which aided in the preparation of the line drawings were graciously provided by the Massachusetts Heritage Program, Maine Critical Areas Program, Les Eastman, Barre Hellquist, Frankie Brackley, George Newman, and the Fish and Wildlife Service. Herbarium specimens also used for the illustrations were provided by the New England Botanical Club Herbarium, the Hodgdon Herbarium of the University of New Hampshire, and the Academy of Natural Sciences of Philadelphia.

TABLE OF CONTENTS

NEW ENGLAND TAXA OF NATIONAL SIGNIFICANCE

FERNS AND FERN ALLIES

Ophioglossaceae

Polypodiaceae

Schizaeaceae

INTRODUCTION

There are several reasons why this report has been published. There are also several aspirations. Congress officially recognized the issue in 1973 declaring in the Endangered Species Act that "... various species of fish, wildlife, and plants in the United States have been rendered extinct as a consequence of economic growth and development untempered by adequate concern and conservation ..." and that others " ... have been so depleted in numbers that they are in danger of or threatened with extinction ...." Although natural phenomena may be contributing factors in a species' demise, the above declaration unfortunately applies all too well to the flora of New England. Residential, industrial and recreational developments and their ancillary demands on a finite land base by an ever increasing population have been and continue to be major influences on the existence and character of New England's flora. Only increased public awareness, concern and conscientious effort by many individuals and organizations will preserve our floristic heritage. That hope is the foundation of this report.

The report is an outgrowth of a cooperative project between the New England Botanical Club's Endangered Species Committee and the U.S. Fish and Wildlife Service's Office of Endangered Species. In the initial phase of the project, the committee members authored individual state reports on rare and endangered plants which the Service published in the fall of 1978: Maine (Eastman, 1978), New Hampshire (Storks and Crow, 1978), Vermont (Countryman, 1978), Massachusetts (Coddington and Field, 1978), Rhode Island (Church and Champlin, 1978), and Connecticut (Mehrhoff, 1978). Several thousand copies of these reports were distributed to the public free upon request.

The state reports and the growing interest in rare plant conservation served as a catalyst for a symposium at Harvard University in May 1979 on New England's rare and endangered plants. The two-day symposium sponsored by the New England Botanical Club and the Service addressed issues concerning 1) biology of endangered species, 2) plant conservation concerns in the New England states and 3) conserving rare plants and their habitats. The proceedings of the symposium were published in the journal **Rhodora** (Vol. 82, no. 829, 1980).

In April 1981 the committee published a list of 479 rare plant taxa pertaining to the entire New England region, including only taxa significant to all of New England (Crow *et al.*, 1981).

New England's Rare, Threatened, and Endangered Plants, based on the regional list, represents a synthesis of the six separate reports and was prepared to focus attention on and provide a more comprehensive assessment of 101 of the rarest plants in New England. Two of the 101 taxa, the Furbish Lousewort *(Pedicularis furbishiae)* and Robbins' Cinquefoil *(Potentilla robbinsiana)*, have been listed under the Endangered Species Act of 1973. Two more taxa, Small Whorled Pogonia *(Isotria medeoloides)* and Silverling *(Paronychia argyrocoma* var. *albimontana)* have been formally proposed for federal listing. An additional 23 taxa which occur in New England are under review by the Service's Office of Endangered Species for possible listing under the Endangered Species Act of 1973 (Federal Register, Vol. 45, No. 242, 15 December 1980).

As a contribution toward a better understanding of those plants presently under review by the U.S. Fish and Wildlife Service, this report provides the following for each taxon: 1) common name and scientific binomial, along with the family, 2) the current status, both federal and the specific New England reports which list the species 3) a description emphasizing the distinctive features accompanied by a detailed pen and ink illustration, 4) the overall distribution, with particular reference to New England and accompanied by a dot map of historical sites documented by herbarium specimens, 5) a description of the habitat, 6) the flowering period, 7) taxonomic comments when appropriate, including synonyms (other scientific names) by which the plant might be known, and 8) selected references which might be useful to the reader. Because a stated purpose of the Endangered Species Act is to preserve the ecosystems upon which endangered and threatened species depend, the report also identifies known or potential threats to New England rare plant populations and, where possible, makes recommendations which might provide a measure of protection to those species and their habitats.

In addition to the 27 plant taxa already listed or under consideration by the U.S. Fish and Wildlife Service, 74 species of "national significance" are included in the report. This group includes many species whose occurrence within New England and the United States is extremely limited, but which may, for instance, be more frequent in arctic regions of North America, and thus may not be eligible for consideration under the Endangered Species Act of 1973. The information presented on these species is largely restricted to habitat and distribution in New England, a dot map showing historical localities and a statement of overall range. Many are illustrated.

The majority of the plants in this report reflect documentation of populations in fewer than ten towns within New England. The criteria applied were largely based on guidelines developed by the Natural Areas Criteria Committee of the New England Botanical Club (Countryman, 1972). Special consideration was given to taxa which presently appear to be on the decline with respect to the number of documented localities, to plants of specialized or vulnerable habitats, to disjuncts. and to endemics. Further attention was given to plants which are likely to be exploited because of particularly appealing features, such as the orchids and ferns.

Although the report presents a great deal of historical and current information on the rarest plants of New England much more remains to be learned. There are many opportunities for individual contributions. Future discoveries of rare plant localities, public education, and specific action in plant conservation and protection are shared responsibilities. This report will hopefully offer encouragement to explore those opportunities.

New England Taxa Listed Under
The Endangered Species Act of 1973

ENDANGERED

FURBISH LOUSEWORT
Pedicularis furbishiae S. Watson

STATUS: U.S. Endangered
New England Reports: ME

FAMILY: Scrophulariaceae (Figwort or Snapdragon Family)

OTHER NAMES: St. John River Wood-betony

DISTINCTIVE FEATURES: The Furbish Lousewort is a tall (4-9 dm) perennial herb. The leaves are stalked, lance-shaped, and deeply divided, with each segment shallowly lobed or toothed and having silvery margins. Flowers occur in a terminal raceme, and are characterized by a calyx with five unequal lobes and greenish-yellow two-lipped corolla; the upper lip of which is straight and lacks a conspicuous beak typical of some other louseworts. The bracts are egg-shaped and toothed. The fruit is a somewhat roundish capsule, about 1.2 cm long, barely exceeding the calyx.

DISTRIBUTION: Map 1. This species is endemic to the banks of the St. John River in Maine and New Brunswick. It was first collected by Kate Furbish in 1880 in Van Buren, Maine and described by Sereno Watson in 1882. Until recent field work (1976-1980) the last collections of the Furbish Lousewort were made in Grand Falls, New Brunswick in 1943 and Ft. Kent, Maine in 1946. The Smithsonian Institution listed *Pedicularis furbishiae* as "probably extinct" in its 1974 report to Congress. However, in July of 1976, Dr. Charles Richards located seven "stations" of *Pedicularis furbishiae* while conducting a rare plant survey on the St. John River for the U.S. Army Corps of Engineers. Additional field surveys were conducted in 1977-1980 by the U.S. Fish and Wildlife Service, the Corps of Engineers, and American and Canadian scientists. The Furbish Lousewort is now known to exist at 28 stations along approximately 140 miles of the St. John River from Andover, New Brunswick upstream to the confluence of the Big Black River in Township 15 Range 13, Maine. The U.S. Fish and Wildlife Service estimates the total population consists of approximately 5,000 individual plants, 72 percent of which occur in the towns of Allagash and St. Francis.

HABITAT: The Furbish Lousewort has a preference for well-drained, sandy loams which are generally low in nitrogen but high in calcium. Soils vary widely in physical and chemical constituents. All but three of the 28 known lousewort stations occur on the north facing river-banks where the species is also often associated with Downy Alder *(Alnus viridis* subsp. *crispa)*. White Spruce *(Picea glauca)*, Balsam Fir *(Abies balsamea)* and various northern hardwoods grow at the top of the broad sloping bank. The herbaceous vegetation along the river banks is very dense. At mid-day the amount of solar radiation on lousewort seedlings and the basal rosette of mature plants measures only ten percent of that in open areas. Lousewort seedlings are in greatest abundance where

Map 1
Pedicularis furbishiae

vegetation is relatively sparse. The plants are root hemi-parasites in the seedling stage, but apparently are not at maturity.

FLOWERING PERIOD: Plants flower from mid-July to mid-August, with seeds dispersing in early September.

ENDANGERMENT: The continued existence of the Furbish Lousewort faces a number of obstacles. Alteration of the riverbank habitat such as cutting of trees, clearing for agricultural use, dumping of trash, and building new homes and camps are major causes of concern. The most notable threat to the species comes from future hydroelectric projects. Based on 1980 field studies, 19 of 28 known lousewort stations were within the proposed impoundments of the Dickey-Lincoln School Lakes Hydroelectric Project. Much of the 66 miles of river that would have been inundated is considered as essential lousewort habitat. Although the Dickey Dam portion of the project has now been deauthorized investigations are continuing on the feasibility of a smaller project at Lincoln School only. However, approximately 60 percent of the known louseworts occur in this area. Two of the Canadian lousewort populations could also become eradicated by modification of the existing hydropower facilities at Grand Falls or the construction of a new facility at Morrill, New Brunswick.

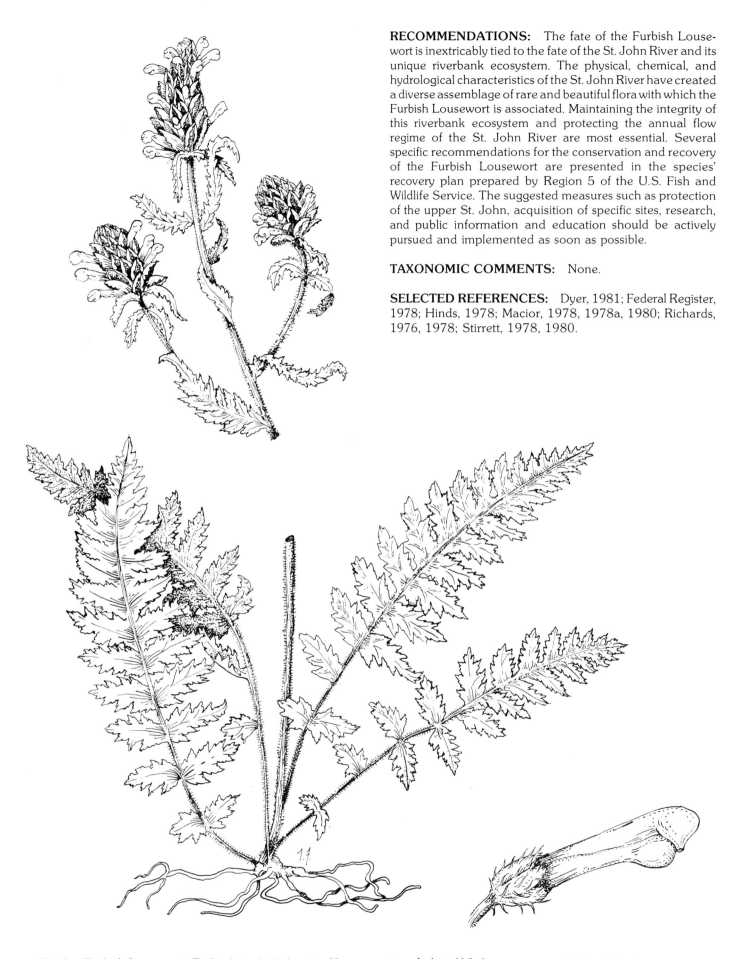

RECOMMENDATIONS: The fate of the Furbish Lousewort is inextricably tied to the fate of the St. John River and its unique riverbank ecosystem. The physical, chemical, and hydrological characteristics of the St. John River have created a diverse assemblage of rare and beautiful flora with which the Furbish Lousewort is associated. Maintaining the integrity of this riverbank ecosystem and protecting the annual flow regime of the St. John River are most essential. Several specific recommendations for the conservation and recovery of the Furbish Lousewort are presented in the species' recovery plan prepared by Region 5 of the U.S. Fish and Wildlife Service. The suggested measures such as protection of the upper St. John, acquisition of specific sites, research, and public information and education should be actively pursued and implemented as soon as possible.

TAXONOMIC COMMENTS: None.

SELECTED REFERENCES: Dyer, 1981; Federal Register, 1978; Hinds, 1978; Macior, 1978, 1978a, 1980; Richards, 1976, 1978; Stirrett, 1978, 1980.

Fig. 1. Furbish Lousewort *(Pedicularis furbishiae)*: Upper portion of plant X.9; lower portion of plant X.9; flower X5.

ROBBINS' CINQUEFOIL
Potentilla robbinsiana Oakes

STATUS: U.S. Endangered
New England Reports: NH, VT (1 historical record)

FAMILY: Rosaceae (Rose Family)

DISTINCTIVE FEATURES: Robbins' Cinquefoil is a small perennial herb which grows in densely tufted rosettes measuring only 2-4 cm across. The crowded leaves are 3-parted and deeply toothed and covered with dense long hairs. The slender flowering stems are 1-3.5 cm high, each bearing a single small yellow flower. The fruits are smooth, plump achenes with a subterminal style which is thickened at the base and recurved at the summit.

DISTRIBUTION: Map 2. This species is presently known from a single site in New Hampshire, on the Monroe Flats, Mt. Washington. Historically, the plant has also been reported from Mt. Lafayette of the Franconia Range with one small site discovered by Endicott on the north side in 1897 and a south station in 1915 by Fernald. A small number of plants were again discovered by Frederic L. Steele at the south station in 1963. Extensive searches for this population have been made by several botanists in recent years, but without success. Steele returned to Mt. Lafayette in 1979 in an attempt to relocate his site, but also failed to find any plants. This site, near the heavily traveled trail is now believed to have been extirpated.

Two additional sites have been documented historically by herbarium specimens collected by Tuckerman; one from the north side of Mt. Washington in 1839 (presently a badly disturbed area in the vicinity of the Auto Road), and the other from Mt. Mansfield, Vermont (but never seen again there).

HABITAT: The plant occurs in the alpine zone growing on an exposed, windswept fellfield of solifluction terraces, stone stripes and soil polygons with a characteristic stony, barren soil devoid of winter snow cover.

Potentilla robbinsiana grows best in the open where the plant cover percentage is low with up to 80% of the surface a stony pavement. It may, on occasion, grow in close proximity to other alpine species. Commonly associated plants include: *Diapensia lapponica, Solidago cutleri, Minuartia (Arenaria) groenlandica, Agrostis borealis, Potentilla tridentata, Vaccinium uliginosum, Loiseleuria procumbens, Rhododendron lapponicum, Juncus trifidus* and *Carex bigelowii.* Robbins' Cinquefoil does not appear to reproduce successfully when crowded.

The stony surface is critical to the suitable habitat. This layer protects the underlying soil from high winds and severe storms that would otherwise blow or wash it away. Spaces between the stones trap and hold fine textured soil and organic particles. These minute sheltered spots serve as nurseries for seedling establishment. The major natural causes of seedling mortality are frost heaving and drought. Most frost heaving occurs in the spring and fall while drought-caused mortality occurs during the summer.

Map 2
Potentilla robbinsiana

Natural migration by Robbins' Cinquefoil is extremely slow. Seed dispersal within the habitat is extremely short ranged. Most seeds drop among the stones adjacent to the parent plant in late July and early August. Some seed transport occurs as a result of raindrop splash and washing during severe summer storms. No new seedlings were discovered more than 14 cm from a seed producing plant. For this reason, the plants tend to be clustered and recolonization of an area where extirpated is extremely slow.

FLOWERING PERIOD: Plants flower for about a 2-week period during mid-June, although single blossoms may occur throughout the season. Fruits develop by mid-July to early August.

ENDANGERMENT: *Potentilla robbinsiana*, with but a single extant population, is critically endangered. Human activities pose the major threat to the survival of the Mt. Washington colony. The Appalachian Trail bisects the fellfield and plants were previously known to occur on both sides of the trail. The size of the population has diminished considerably, now occupying about one-quarter of the territory it occupied in 1934 according to Steele.

In a 1980 survey of hiker activity conducted by G. E. Crow and R. E. Graber in the area designated as Critical Habitat by the U.S. Fish and Wildlife Service, hiker traffic on and adjacent to the plant habitat was estimated at 7535 people per year. About 10% of the hikers left the trail and had a negative impact on the population. Approximately 34% of the hikers walking on the habitat were there to see the plant while most of the remaining were there because the trail passed through the area.

Fig. 2. Robbins' Cinquefoil *(Potentilla robbinsiana)*: Habit X1.5; X1.

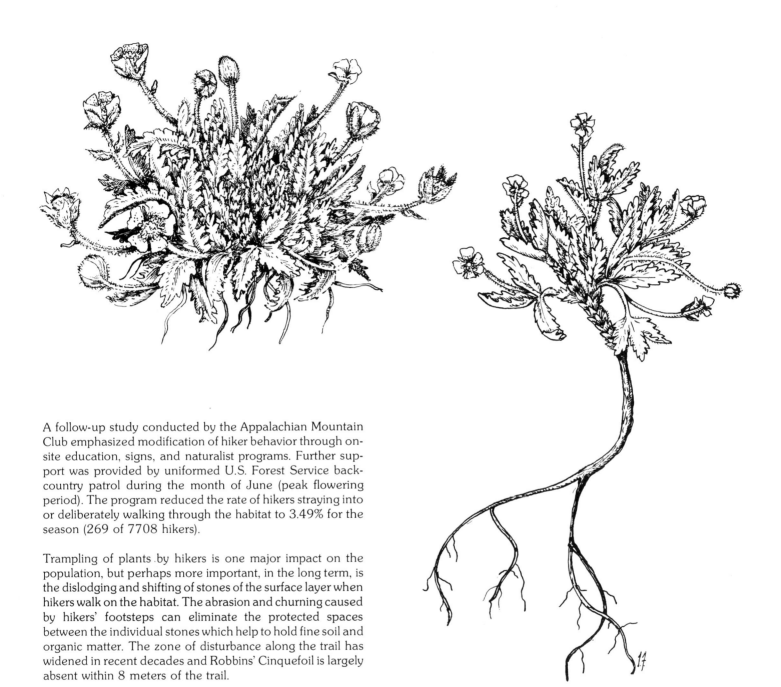

A follow-up study conducted by the Appalachian Mountain Club emphasized modification of hiker behavior through on-site education, signs, and naturalist programs. Further support was provided by uniformed U.S. Forest Service backcountry patrol during the month of June (peak flowering period). The program reduced the rate of hikers straying into or deliberately walking through the habitat to 3.49% for the season (269 of 7708 hikers).

Trampling of plants by hikers is one major impact on the population, but perhaps more important, in the long term, is the dislodging and shifting of stones of the surface layer when hikers walk on the habitat. The abrasion and churning caused by hikers' footsteps can eliminate the protected spaces between the individual stones which help to hold fine soil and organic matter. The zone of disturbance along the trail has widened in recent decades and Robbins' Cinquefoil is largely absent within 8 meters of the trail.

RECOMMENDATIONS: Preservation of the habitat is essential for survival of Robbins' Cinquefoil. Hiker activity in the area remains problematic. Educational programs involving naturalists stationed at the nearby AMC Lakes-of-the-Clouds Hut should be continued. Transplant stations need to be maintained as displays for "plant lovers" to allow observation of the plant without impacting the natural population. Some relocation of the Crawford Path to by-pass the habitat is viewed as an important component of the effort to preserve the present colony. If the trail is relocated and the present trail closed, the area for potential recolonization within the present site would be increased to its original size. This may be critical for long term preservation of the species. It would also be desirable to declare the immediate Monroe Flats area a Research Area.

TAXONOMIC COMMENTS: This taxon is viewed by Löve and Löve as an apomictic segregate of the arctic taxon *Potentilla hyparctica* Malte. According to their viewpoint the name *P. robbinsiana* Oakes subsp. *robbinsiana* must be applied to the Mt. Washington taxon and *P. robbinsiana* subsp. *hyparctica* (Malte) D. Löve applied to the arctic plant.

SELECTED REFERENCES: Countryman, 1980; Crow and Graber, 1981, 1981a; Crow and Storks, 1980; Crow *et al.* 1981; Federal Register, 1980; Graber, 1980; Graber and Crow, 1982; Löve and Löve, 1966; Löve, 1968; Pease, 1917; Steele, 1964; Storks and Crow, 1978, 1979; Taylor, 1981; Torrey and Gray, 1840.

SMALL WHORLED POGONIA
Isotria medeoloides

STATUS: U.S. Endangered
New England Reports: ME, NH, VT, MA, RI, CT

FAMILY: ORCHIDACEAE (Orchid Family)

DISTINCTIVE FEATURES: Small Whorled Pogonia is a perennial herb which grows through the leaf litter from a cluster of short thickened roots, producing a single stem from a short, vertical rhizome. A whorl of 5-6 leaves occurs near the summit of the stem; the leaves are narrow, oblong or slightly broader toward the leaf tip and 3.5-6.0 cm long with the whole whorl reflexed in bud, gradually straightening in flower and fruit. The leaves and stem have a grayish-green appearance due to a waxy substance on the surface. The flowers are usually solitary, but in some populations double flowered plants may predominate. The flower is light green to yellow-green and borne on a peduncle which is shorter than the ovary. The sepals are linear-lanceolate, 16-20 mm long, arching forward but only slightly exceeding the lip and column. The narrow petals widen somewhat toward the tip (narrowly obovate), 10-15 mm long. The lip is 3-lobed, about 1 cm long and not spurred.

Isotria medeoloides is readily distinguished from *Isotria verticillata* (Whorled Pogonia) with the latter characterized by darker green stems and leaves, flowers with a purplish-brown color, sepals very narrow and greatly exceeding the lip and column (3-6 cm long) and a peduncle clearly longer than the ovary.

DISTRIBUTION: Map 3. This species occurs very locally and extremely infrequently from New England to southern Ontario, southwestern Michigan, southern Illinois, southeastern Missouri and south to southeastern New York, New Jersey, Pennsylvania, Maryland, Virginia, North Carolina, South Carolina, and possibly Georgia.

HABITAT: Small Whorled Pogonia grows in somewhat open mixed hardwood forest; beech-birch-maple or oak-hickory southward and in mixed beech, oak, and hemlock woods northward. The plants seem to prefer rich, subacid soils, emerging in dry to moist leaf mould. It frequently grows in association with a very similar herb, *Medeola virginiana* (Indian Cucumber or Cucumber Root), the latter being readily distinguished in the sterile state by its cob-webby stem.

FLOWERING PERIOD: Late May to mid-June.

ENDANGERMENT: This species is extremely rare throughout its range and is probably the rarest orchid species in northeastern North America. While it has been known historically from about 60 sites (49 counties in 17 states and 1 county in Ontario, Canada), today it has been verified as

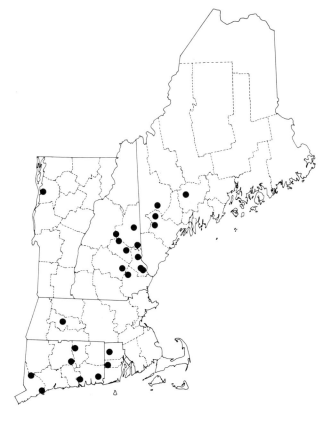

Map 3
Isotria medeoloides

extant in only 15 of these sites. These populations consist of very small numbers of plants, usually fewer than 30. One unusually large colony of 190 plants is known in Maine.

RECOMMENDATIONS: Due to the extreme rarity of this orchid, the documented taking of plant specimens (numerous herbarium specimens), and the great interest by wildflower enthusiasts, orchid fanciers and botanists, Critical Habitat has purposely not been proposed by the U.S. Fish and Wildlife Service. It is important, however, to monitor the known extant stations for possible impact. In New Hampshire a recently relocated population of *Isotria medeoloides* occurs within a short distance of a new highway. This population should be watched for such adverse effects as highway salt damage.

TAXONOMIC COMMENTS:
Synonyms: *Pogonia affinis* Austin ex Gray
               Isotria affinis (Austin ex Gray) Rydberg

SELECTED REFERENCES: Baldwin, 1884; Brackley, 1981; Case and Schwab, 1971; Church, 1980; Correll, 1950; Eames, 1926; Eastman, 1977a; Federal Register, 1980a; Grimes, 1921; Lownes, 1917; Luer, 1975; Mehrhoff, 1980, 1980a, 1980b; Sheviak, 1974; Stewart, 1978.

Fig. 3. Small Whorled Pogonia *(Isotria medeoloides)*: Flowering habit X1; fruiting habit X.8.

SILVERLING
Paronychia argyrocoma (Michx.) Nutt.
var. *albimontana* Fern.

STATUS: U.S. Threatened
New England Reports: ME, NH, MA

FAMILY: Caryophyllaceae (Pink Family)

OTHER NAMES: Silver Whitlow-wort.

DISTINCTIVE FEATURES: Silverling is a small, tufted perennial herb. The freely branching stems bear pairs of small flat, linear leaves with elongated stipules. The numerous small flowers are densely aggregated at the tops of the stems and are hidden by conspicuous silvery bracts. Plants occur singly or in small groups and occasionally in somewhat large colonies. This variety is distinguished from var. *argyrocoma*, a plant of the Southern Appalachians, by having leaves which become glabrous and have inrolled margins, a lax cymose inflorescence, a smaller calyx (3.3-4.0 mm) which is less pubescent.

DISTRIBUTION: Map 4. Variety *albimontana* (meaning of the White Mountains) has a very restricted overall distribution and occurs very locally throughout its range. It is chiefly known from the White Mountains of New Hampshire, but also occurs in the mountains of western Maine and a single station on an island in the Merrimack River, Massachusetts. One historical record (no date) has been documented from Vermont (no specific locality) by a specimen on deposit in the herbarium of the Concord Field Station, Harvard University.

HABITAT: Silverling grows on open dry granitic rock ledges, generally in rock crevices and rooted in thin, gravelly soil.

FLOWERING PERIOD: Plants flower from July through August. The species is most easily recognized during this period by the silvery bracts surrounding the flowers and capsules.

ENDANGERMENT: Colonies are exposed to harsh weather conditions and heavy hiker traffic. Many of the 13 extant sites occur atop frequently-visited mountains.

RECOMMENDATIONS: Critical Habitat has not been proposed by the U.S. Fish and Wildlife Service in order to avoid calling attention to this small attractive plant, thereby increasing potential trampling of the very fragile sites. Since the colonies often occur near trails it is important for personnel involved in trail upkeep to be aware of the existence of Silverling populations to prevent accidental destruction of sites.

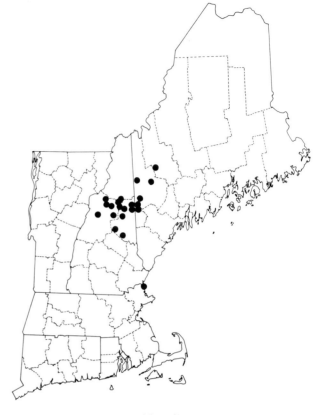

Map 4
Paronychia argyrocoma var. *albimontana*

TAXONOMIC COMMENTS:
Synonym: *Paronychia argyrocoma* subsp. *albimontana* (Fernald) Löve and Löve

SELECTED REFERENCES: Chaudhri, 1968; Clarkson *et al.*, 1981; Crow and Storks, 1980; Federal Register, 1980b; Fernald, 1906; Löve and Löve, 1965; Storks and Crow, 1979.

Fig. 4. Silverling *(Paronychia argyrocoma* var. *albimontana)*: Habit X1; flower cluster X4; flower X5.-

SANDPLAIN GERARDIA
Agalinis acuta Pennell

STATUS: U.S., 1980 FR Notice of Review
New England Reports: MA, RI, CT

FAMILY: Scrophulariaceae (Figwort or Snapdragon Family)

DISTINCTIVE FEATURES: *Agalinis acuta* is a light green annual herb with a weakly angular, little-branched stem, growing between 1-2 dm (occasionally 4 dm) tall. The leaves are opposite, linear and scabrous (rough) above, up to 2.5 cm long. The flowers are borne in racemes of 2-8 flowers each subtended by a bract. The somewhat bell-shaped flowers are pink-purple with 2 cream-colored lines and purple spots in the corolla throat, the corolla tube 7-9 mm long, and corolla lobes 3-4 mm long, shallowly notched or truncate at the tip. The calyx is bell-shaped, bearing sharp, triangular teeth, and is nearly three-fourths the length of the ovoid capsule. The seeds are small (0.4-0.6 mm) with a conspicuously reticulate surface pattern.

DISTRIBUTION: Map 5. Sandplain Gerardia has a very restricted overall distribution, limited to the Coastal Plain of Massachusetts, Rhode Island, Connecticut and Long Island, New York. Most stations are reported from southeastern Massachusetts.

HABITAT: The plant grows in dry, sandy soils of roadsides, sandy plains, and oak scrub openings.

FLOWERING PERIOD: Late August to late September; fruiting September to October.

ENDANGERMENT: Habitat succession appears to be the major threat to the disappearance of the Sandplain Gerardia as factors which kept the sand plains open, such as fire and grazing, are largely absent. Development also appears to be a threat for *Agalinis acuta*. Most records of this species date back to the late 1800's and early 1900's. Recent field work suggests that many of these populations have been extirpated. It is believed to be extinct in Rhode Island and no sites have been relocated in Connecticut. Two stations have been newly discovered by Bruce Sorrie on Cape Cod, Massachusetts in 1980-1981. Further field work has failed to relocate other Massachusetts sites. New York reports that the species is probably extinct on Long Island due to development and overgrown habitats.

RECOMMENDATIONS: The extant stations persist at cemeteries. On September 8, 1980 approximately 40 small plants were noted at one station flowering in the short grass. A week later the area had been mowed and no plants were spotted. In 1981, plants were again seen at this locality but mostly at different sections of the site. Since this species is an

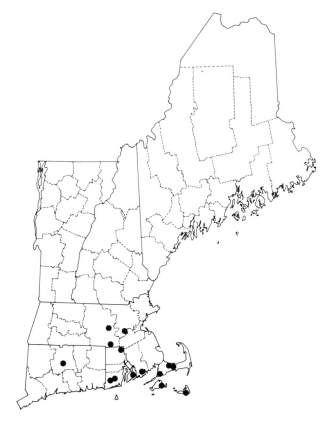

Map 5
Agalinis acuta

annual it is essential to allow plants to flower and seeds to mature. It is advisable to refrain from mowing this section, especially from July through October.

TAXONOMIC COMMENTS:
Synonyms: *Gerardia acuta* (Pennell) Pennell

Although the generic name *Gerardia* appears in many manuals, it has been misapplied to these members of the family Scrophulariaceae. Linnaeus applied the name *Gerardia* to plants in another family (Acanthaceae). While the next oldest name available was *Chytra* it was obscure and the name *Agalinis* has been formally conserved; it is therefore the correct name (see International Code of Botanical Nomenclature).

SELECTED REFERENCES: Canne, 1979; Coddington and Field, 1978; Eastman, 1978; Mitchell *et al.*, 1980; Pennell, 1929, 1935; Stafleu *et al.*, 1978.

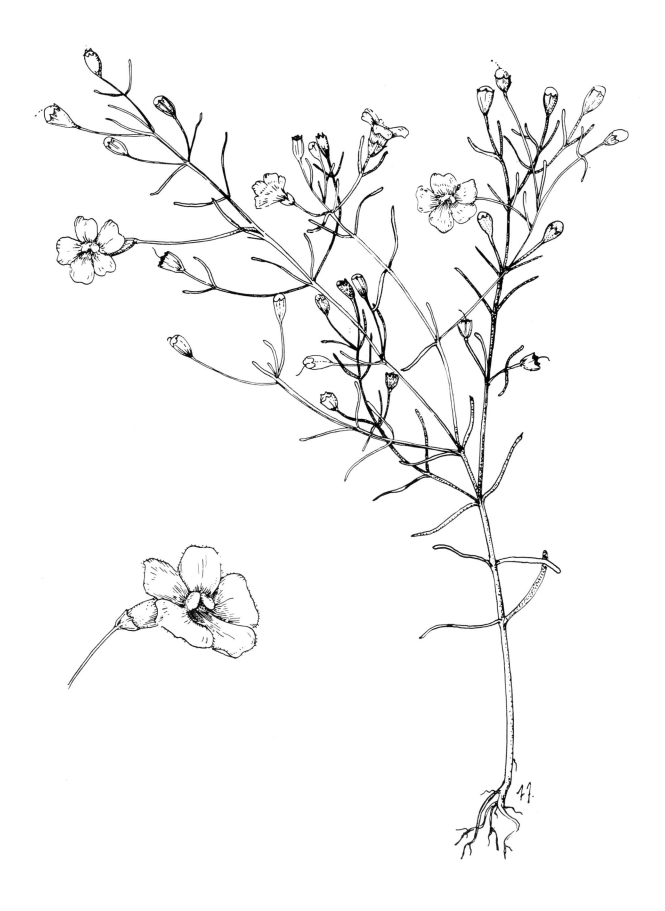

Fig. 5.   Sandplain Gerardia *(Agalinis acuta)*: Habit X1; flower X2.

JESUP'S MILK-VETCH
Astragalus robbinsii (Oakes) Gray
var. *jesupi* Eggl. and Sheld.

STATUS: U.S., 1980 FR Notice of Review
New England Reports: NH, VT

FAMILY: Leguminosae/Fabaceae (Pea or Bean Family)

DISTINCTIVE FEATURES: Jesup's Milk-vetch is a perennial herb growing from rhizomes. The stems are single or few, reaching 2-6 dm tall and are smooth or sparsely covered with closely appressed hairs. The leaves are pinnately compound, the leaflets 9-17 in number and oblong to elliptic, 1-2 cm long, and glabrous or sparsely covered with appressed hairs. The flowers, borne in racemes, are violet or bluish-purple, 9-17 mm long. The calyx lobes are awl-shaped and half as long as the calyx tube. The fruit is a legume which tapers at both ends, the body 1.4-2.1 cm long, 2.5 mm wide and sparsely covered with black, appressed hairs.

DISTRIBUTION: Map 6. This taxon is entirely restricted to an area a few miles long on both banks of the Connecticut River at Hartland, Vermont and Plainfield and Claremont, New Hampshire.

HABITAT: Jesup's Milk-vetch grows along the riverbanks in moist crevices of shelving rocks just above high water and sometimes in the shade of overhanging shrubs.

FLOWERING PERIOD: Late May to July.

ENDANGERMENT: The most notable threat comes from future hydroelectric development.

RECOMMENDATIONS: Stations should be monitored to insure preservation of the habitat.

TAXONOMIC COMMENTS:
Synonym: *Astragalus jesupi* (Eggl. and Sheld.) Britt.

SELECTED REFERENCES: Barneby, 1964; Countryman 1978; Storks and Crow, 1978.

Map 6
Astragalus robbinsii var. *jesupi*

Fig. 6. Jesup's Milk-vetch *(Astragalus robbinsii* var. *jesupi)*: Habit X1; fruit cluster X1; single fruit X3.

NEW ENGLAND ROCK-CRESS
Braya humilis (C. A. Meyer) Robinson
var. *leiocarpa* (Trautv.) Fern.

STATUS: U.S., 1980 FR Notice of Review
New England Reports: VT

FAMILY: Cruciferae/Brassicaceae (Mustard Family)

DISTINCTIVE FEATURES: New England Rock-cress is a perennial plant from a short stout stem, forming a basal rosette of leaves. The basal leaves are thin and slightly toothed or wavy, either glabrous or hairy. Several stems arise from the rosette, typically reaching 10-20 (-37) cm in height with scattered narrow leaves; blades with toothed or entire margins. The flowers are white to slightly purplish, with petals 3.2-4.2 mm long, borne in a compact raceme. The fruits (siliques) are long and narrow (14-20 mm long, 0.7-0.8 mm wide), and lose their hairiness, becoming smooth at maturity. The stigma is distinctly capitate. It is the smooth fruit that particularly sets var. *leiocarpa* apart from other varieties of the species.

DISTRIBUTION: Map 7. While *Braya humilis* is a circumpolar species occurring in arctic and alpine regions, var. *leiocarpa* is very restricted in its range. Although Fernald gives the range as northern Vermont and the Lake Superior region of Ontario, Abbe recognizes the Vermont station as a race separate from his five other races of the species in northeastern North America. Böcher has likewise recognized the plants at the single site in Vermont as distinct enough to warrant recognition at the species level *(Braya novae-angliae)*. Argus and White do not include *Braya humilis* in their list of rare plants of Ontario and Porsild and Cody's distribution map of *Braya humilis* does not include any sites in the Lake Superior region of Canada. Michigan, however, does include *Braya humilis* on its list of rare and endangered plants, but no varietal status is indicated.

HABITAT: This rock-cress grows only on calcareous cliffs and talus.

FLOWERING PERIOD: June-July.

ENDANGERMENT: The population on the Willoughby Cliffs appears to be vigorous and does not presently seem threatened. Many plants occur on inaccessible faces of the cliffs.

RECOMMENDATIONS: Periodic monitoring is desirable.

TAXONOMIC COMMENTS:
Synonyms: *Braya novae-angliae* (Rydb.) Th. Sorensen
Braya humilis var. *novae-angliae* (Rydb.) Fern.
Pilosella novae-angliae Rydb.
Arabidopsis novae-angliae Britt.

The species is in a very complicated group of very closely related taxa and needs to be studied from a world-wide perspective. Although Abbe's treatment of the Brayas of boreal eastern America recognizes six races in this region, it fails to designate taxonomic status to these races.

Map 7
Braya humilis var. *leiocarpa*

SELECTED REFERENCES: Abbe, 1948; Argus and White, 1977; Böcher, 1956; Fernald, 1937a, 1950; Porsild and Cody, 1980; Rollins, 1953; Wagner *et al.*, 1977.

14

Fig. 7.   New England Rock-cress *(Braya humilis* var. *leiocarpa)*: Habit X1; fruit X4; flower X4.

LONG'S BITTER CRESS
Cardamine longii Fern.

STATUS: U.S., 1980 FR Notice of Review
New England Reports: ME

FAMILY: Cruciferae/Brassicaceae (Mustard Family)

DISTINCTIVE FEATURES: Long's Bitter Cress is a weak-stemmed perennial, growing prostrate to erect. The stem is smooth at the base in contrast to the stiff hairs present in *Cardamine pensylvanica*. The leaves are simple and kidney-shaped to nearly round with a heart-shaped base. The flowers have no petals and are somewhat inconspicuous, 0.7-1.2 mm long, borne in a few flowered raceme. The fruits are lance-shaped siliques, 5-10 mm long. The seeds are elliptical, yellow with a brown margin, 1.2 mm long, 0.8 mm wide.

DISTRIBUTION: Map 8. An estuary plant, Long's Bitter Cress has been reported from only four coastal sites in Maine, from Long Island, New York and from a few sites in the estuaries of Chesapeake Bay in Maryland and Virginia.

HABITAT: The single confirmed New England site, along the Cathance River, Bowdoinham, Maine, occurs on tidal banks and muck-covered ledges shaded by Northern White Cedar *(Thuja occidentalis)* and Yellow Birch *(Betula alleghaniensis)*. The plants experience inundation twice daily.

FLOWERING PERIOD: Late June-July; fruiting in August and September.

ENDANGERMENT: None at present.

RECOMMENDATIONS: Periodic monitoring of the site is desirable.

TAXONOMIC COMMENTS: The taxonomic status of this plant requires investigation. L. M. Eastman suggests that this may be just a growth form of *Cardamine pensylvanica* whose morphological expression is greatly influenced by tidal action.

SELECTED REFERENCES: Broom *et al.*, 1979; Critical Areas Program, 1981; Eastman, 1976a; Fernald, 1917, 1942; Mitchell *et al.*, 1980; Porter, 1979.

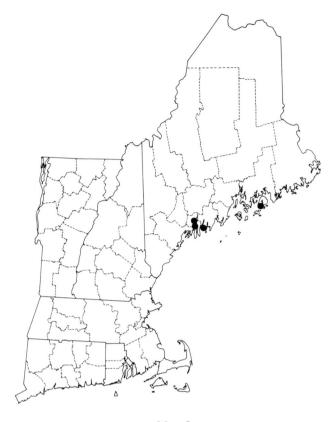

Map 8
Cardamine longii

Fig. 8. Long's Bitter Cress *(Cardamine longii)*: Habit X1; fruit X4.

17

ORONO SEDGE
Carex oronensis Fern.

STATUS: U.S., 1980 FR Notice of Review
New England Reports: ME

FAMILY: Cyperaceae (Sedge Family)

DISTINCTIVE FEATURES: Orono Sedge grows in loose clumps, producing sharply angled stems, 0.5-1 m tall. The leaves are much shorter than the stem, the principal leaf blades 3-5 mm wide, the bases lacking auricles. Fruits are clustered into dense heads with 3-9 thick, cylindric to ellipsoid or lance-shaped heads (2-3 cm long) per spike. The scales subtending the fruits and flowers are dark, with pale white translucent (hyaline) margins and a conspicuous midvein. The perigynia (envelopes surrounding the achenes) are somewhat lance-shaped, 4-4.5 mm long, 0.7-1.5 mm wide and tapering to a subacute, prolonged base and narrow beak, scarcely winged below the middle.

DISTRIBUTION: Map 9. Orono Sedge is endemic to the Penobscot River Valley in the vicinity of Orono, Maine. Only one site has been recently verified.

HABITAT: Fields, meadows and clearings are the typical habitats as well as occasionally bordering alluvial woods.

FLOWERING PERIOD: June; fruiting July-August (fruits essential for correct identification).

ENDANGERMENT: None at present.

RECOMMENDATIONS: A single station was relocated at Pea Cove, Old Town, Maine where only one large mature plant was found growing in a dry, open field (July 1978, by L. M. Eastman and D. Burdick). If the area remains as it is there appears to be no threat to survival.

TAXONOMIC COMMENTS: This taxon requires careful examination as to its taxonomic status as a species. It may be a hybrid.

SELECTED REFERENCES: Eastman, 1980; Fernald, 1902; Mackenzie, 1940.

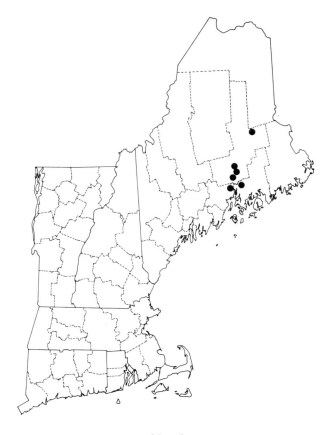

Map 9
Carex oronensis

18

Fig. 9.   Orono Sedge *(Carex oronensis)*: Habit X1; cluster of spikelets X1; individual spikelet X3; bract X12; perigynium X12; achene X12.

NEW ENGLAND THOROUGHWORT
Eupatorium leucolepis (DC.) Torrey and Gray
var. *novae-angliae* Fern.

STATUS: U.S., 1980 FR Notice of Review
New England Reports: MA, RI

FAMILY: Compositae/Asteraceae (Aster or Sunflower Family)

DISTINCTIVE FEATURES: *Eupatorium leucolepis* var. *novae-angliae* is a tall, stiffly erect perennial herb, reaching from (0.3-) 0.5-1.3 m in height. The leaves, which lack a petiole, are narrow (0.8-2 cm wide) and taper to an acute tip. The leaf margins are sharply toothed and the undersurface is covered with short, soft, curved hairs. The stem is weakly hairy. The flowers occur in heads which are arranged in flat-topped clusters (corymb), with heads containing three to seven white flowers. The scales (phyllaries) around the heads are covered with matted white hairs and have conspicuous white-scarious sharp tips.

Variety *novae-angliae* is especially distinguished from var. *leucolepis* by having leaves which are sharply toothed and having somewhat longer hairs; the leaves are also flat (rather that plicate) and markedly broader, tapering to an acute tip (not blunt).

DISTRIBUTION: Map 10. A New England endemic, var. *novae-angliae* has been reported from 11 sites in Plymouth Co., Massachusetts and from 5 sites in Washington Co., and 1 site in Newport Co., Rhode Island.

HABITAT: The plants typically grow on gently sloping sandy or peaty shores of Coastal Plain ponds which have incomplete or no drainage and are subject to greatly fluctuating water levels.

FLOWERING PERIOD: Late August to early October.

ENDANGERMENT: Populations from four historical localities have been extirpated, and a fifth, the type locality, is nearly so. Threats to survival include alteration of pond shores by development, recreational activities, and natural processes of succession to woody vegetation, and alteration of water table. Planned highway construction threatens a large population in Kingston, Massachusetts.

RECOMMENDATIONS: None of the extant populations is protected. Land acquisition appears to be the most desirable method of preservation. Two large populations in Plymouth Co., Massachusetts may be the best candidates for preservation by land acquisition. At present none of the sites is permanently preserved.

TAXONOMIC COMMENTS: None.

SELECTED REFERENCES: Church, 1980; Coddington and Field, 1978; Fernald, 1937; Field and Coddington, 1980; Sinnott, 1912; Sorrie, 1981.

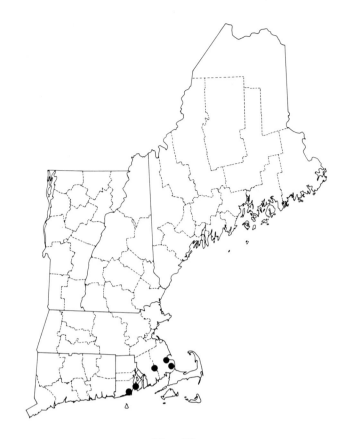

Map 10
Eupatorium leucoplepis var. *novae-angliae*

Fig. 10. New England Thoroughwort *(Eupatorium leucolepis* var. *novae-angliae)*: Habit X.9; head of flowers X3; achene X3; phyllary X6.

BUSHY ROCKROSE
Helianthemum dumosum (Bickn.) Fern.

STATUS: U.S., 1980 FR Notice of Review
New England Reports: MA, RI, CT

FAMILY: Cistaceae (Rockrose Family)

DISTINCTIVE FEATURES: Bushy Rockrose is a loosely branched perennial herb (1-25 cm tall) with stems ascending, soon branching almost horizontal, forming compact to diffuse low, bushy mounds. The pubescence on the stems, leaves and capsules consist of dense stellate hairs intermixed with reddish glandular hairs. Flowers with pale yellow petals occur singly near the tips of the main branches; the sepals bear red papillae among pale hairs. Growth of branches continues and cleistogamous flowers (which lack petals and pollinate themselves without opening) develop at the forks and tips of leafy branchlets. The fruits derived from the earlier flowers begin to mature as the cleistogamous flowers start to appear. The capsules derived from cleistogamous flowers are much smaller than those from the large, showy flowers. The seeds are about as long as broad, with pebbled surfaces.

Helianthemum canadense, a very similar species, is more erect, with a well developed central axis and less branching (not mound forming), has less dense and coarse pubescence, and seeds longer than thick, with long papillae.

DISTRIBUTION: Map 11. *Helianthemum dumosum* is a Coastal Plain species which is endemic to southeastern New England and Long Island, New York.

HABITAT: Characteristic habitat includes open, dry sandy soil and dry, open sandy woods. Much natural habitat has been lost and recent occurrences are often found in artificially-maintained "sand plains" such as airport runway borders, golf courses, and cemeteries.

FLOWERING PERIOD: Flowers with petals occur late May to late June; cleistogamous flowers from July-September.

ENDANGERMENT: The chief threat to survival may be loss of habitat due to natural succession. Development on the sandy barren sites also represents a potential problem. However, no clear threats are presently known and the species appears vigorous at a number of sites.

RECOMMENDATIONS: Monitoring would be desirable, especially on selected undisturbed sites to observe habitat succession and the species' response.

TAXONOMIC COMMENTS: None

SELECTED REFERENCES: Daoud and Wilbur, 1965.

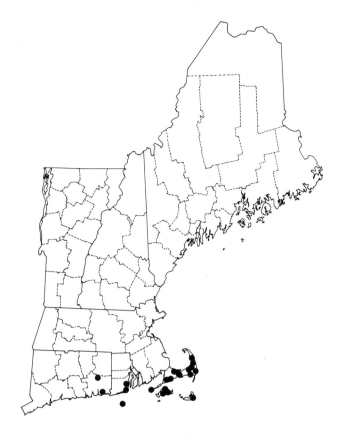

Map 11
Helianthemum dumosum

Fig. 11. Bushy Rockrose *(Helianthemum dumosum)*: Habit X1 showing progressive growth (right to left) through the season; open flower X3; fruit derived from open flower X3; cleistogamous flower X5.

EATON'S QUILLWORT
Isoetes eatonii Dodge

STATUS: U.S., 1980 FR Notice of Review
New England Reports: NH, MA, CT

FAMILY: Isoetaceae (Quillwort Family)

DISTINCTIVE FEATURES: Eaton's Quillwort, a fern ally, is a perennial aquatic or amphibious herb which forms grass-like tufts. The long, quill-like, tapering leaves arise from the crown of a fleshy corm in an erect to arching or recurved manner. The sporangia, located at the base of the leaves, are 6-11 mm long, brown-spotted to wholly brown, and partially covered by a thin, membranous vellum. The megaspores (female), essential for identification, are 300-520 microns in diameter, with high, irregular, nearly contiguous ridges on the upper half; the faces covered by labyrinthiform-convolute ridges. The microspores (male), scattered among the mega-spores, are only 25-35 microns in diameter and smooth or minutely tuberculate.

DISTRIBUTION: Map 12. Eaton's Quillwort grows in scattered locations from southern New Hampshire to New Jersey. A new station has been reported from Ontario. Few New England sites have been relocated.

HABITAT: The plants grow in shallow water or muddy borders of ponds and streams.

SPORULATING PERIOD: August-September.

ENDANGERMENT: The major threats to populations are water pollution and habitat modification due to urbanization and flood control.

RECOMMENDATIONS: Extant stations should be monitored.

TAXONOMIC COMMENTS: None.

SELECTED REFERENCES: Kott and Bobbette, 1980; Pfeiffer, 1922.

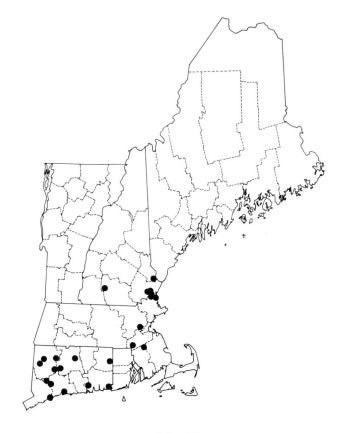

Map 12
Isoetes eatonii

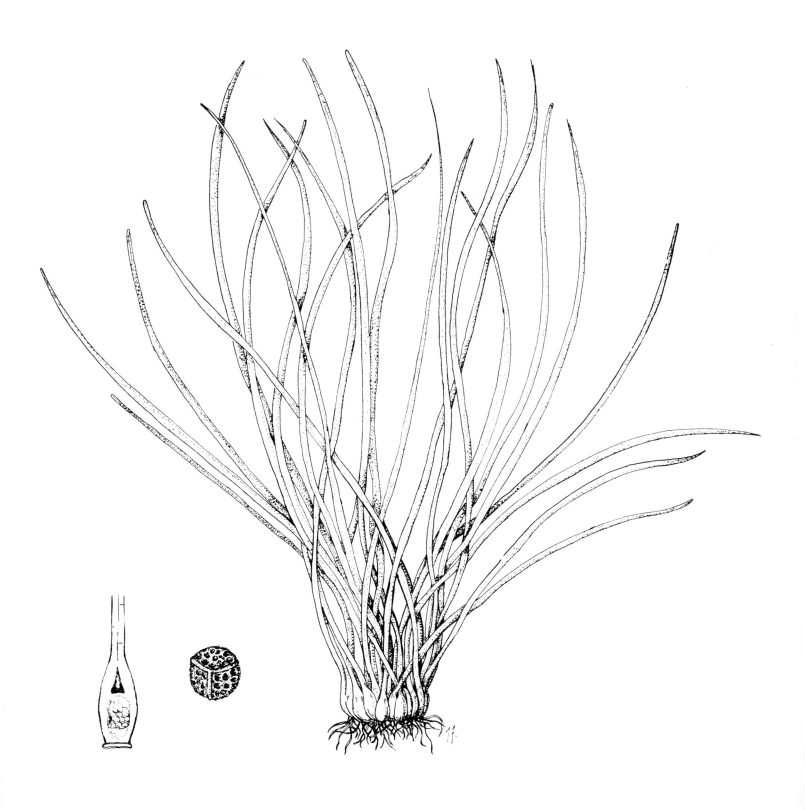

Fig. 12.   Eaton's Quillwort *(Isoetes eatonii)*: Habit X1; fertile leaf base with sporangia X4; megaspore X30.

AURICLED TWAYBLADE
Listera auriculata Wieg.

STATUS: U.S., 1980 FR Notice of Review
New England Reports: ME, NH, VT

FAMILY: Orchidaceae (Orchid Family)

DISTINCTIVE FEATURES: The Auricled Twayblade is a small, erect, unbranched perennial herb. The short stem (4-25 cm high) bears a pair of sessile, oval leaves 1.5-6.5 cm long. The flowers are small and greenish, occurring along a loose raceme. The flowers resemble, to some degree, large winged insects scattered along a stem. They are composed of a large notched lower lip with a narrow groove which secretes nectar, and a pair of characteristic small, curved "ears" (auricles) at the top of the lip clasping the column. The lip is broadest at the base and is slightly constricted in the middle and is notched only about one-fourth the length of the lip. A similar twayblade, *Listera convallarioides*, lacks auricles and the lip is broadest at the top. *Listera australis* has "ears" but the column is very short (up to 1.0 mm) and the lower lip is deeply cleft. *Listera cordata* also has a very short column and a deeply cleft lip, but lacks auricles. *Listera borealis*, which sometimes grows with *Listera auriculata* has oblong auricles which diverge from the column rather than curving behind the column.

DISTRIBUTION: Map 13. The species is found in northeastern North America from Newfoundland to the Thunder Bay District, Ontario and western Manitoba (Singush Lake); it occurs more widespread in the St. Lawrence Region.

HABITAT: Auricled Twayblade grows in calcareous alluvial soils in low woods, alder thickets and in Northern White Cedar swamps. Plants tend to develop best at about the high flood water line.

FLOWERING PERIOD: Plants flower for a short period from mid-June to mid-July. Identification is difficult without flowers.

ENDANGERMENT: *Listera auriculata* is considered threatened due to its extreme rarity; only two extant sites are known in New England. Its preferred habitat tends to be unstable. This is a natural contributing factor to its rarity.

RECOMMENDATIONS: Known localities should be protected from activities which would disrupt the habitat. Trail sites adjacent to colonies should be shifted away from the immediate area.

SELECTED REFERENCES: Brackley, 1981; Cody and Munro, 1980; Eastman, 1977; Morris and Eames, 1929; Nylander, 1921; Wallace, 1951; Whiting and Catling, 1977; Wiegand, 1899.

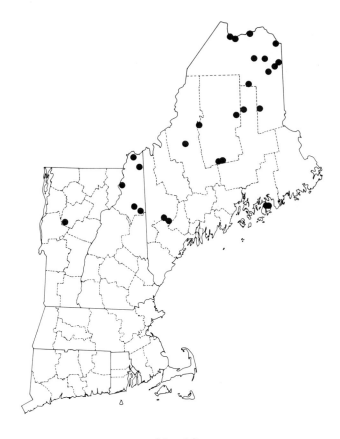

Map 13
Listera auriculata

Fig. 13.   Auricled Twayblade *(Listera auriculata)*: Habit X1; flower X5.

ESTUARINE MONKEY-FLOWER
Mimulus ringens L.
var. *colpophilus* Fern.

STATUS: U.S., 1980 FR Notice of Review
New England Reports: ME

FAMILY: Scrophulariaceae (Figwort or Snapdragon Family)

DISTINCTIVE FEATURES: Estuarine Monkey-flower is a perennial herb with an erect stem, about 4-13 cm tall, growing from a creeping rhizome. The leaves are borne opposite on a square stem, mostly clasping or strongly rounded at the base, lacking a petiole. The leaf blades are oblong, elliptical, oblanceolate or narrowly obovate, with a shallowly toothed margin. The flowers are blue-violet or pinkish, about 2 cm long, the corolla throat nearly closed by the large palate. The calyx, 0.8-2 cm long, is tubular and the fruit, a capsule, remains enclosed within the strongly angled calyx. Variety *colpophilus* is distinguished from the typical by having shorter internodes (1.5-2.5 cm long) and much smaller principal leaves (2.5-5 cm long) and smaller flowers.

DISTRIBUTION: Map 14. Variety *colpophilus* is restricted to estuaries of the St. Lawrence River System, Quebec and coastal Maine.

HABITAT: Muddy banks and gravelly shores of estuaries.

FLOWERING PERIOD: June.

ENDANGERMENT: Only six historic sites are known for New England; only one Maine station has been verified extant.

RECOMMENDATIONS: The single known population should be monitored and additional field checking for further sites is needed.

TAXONOMIC COMMENTS: This plant requires further study regarding its taxonomic status. Pennell suggests its reduced floral morphology, coupled with self-pollination, is typical of other Scrophulariaceous plants growing in estuarine sites and that careful field observations are needed. Les Eastman has suggested that this plant may be nothing more than a phenological expression in response to submergence by tidal waters twice daily, thus representing an ecological form unworthy of taxonomic recognition.

SELECTED REFERENCES: Eastman, 1980; Fernald, 1950; Pennell, 1935.

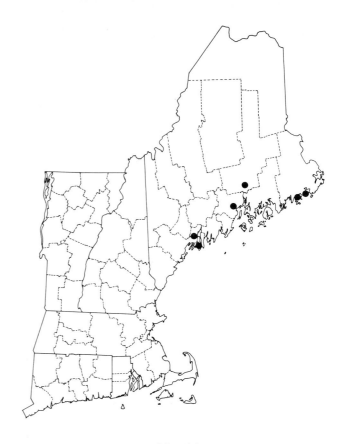

Map 14
Mimulus ringens var. *colpophilus*

28

Fig. 14. Estuarine Monkey-flower *(Mimulus ringens* var. *colpophilus)*: Habit X.9; flower X3.

SERPENTINE SANDWORT
Minuartia marcescens (Fern.) House

STATUS: U.S., 1980 FR Notice of Review
New England Reports: VT

FAMILY: Caryophyllaceae (Pink Family)

DISTINCTIVE FEATURES: Serpentine Sandwort is a densely matted plant with trailing and freely branching stems which are covered with rigid remnants of previous years' leaves (marcescent). The linear leaves are slightly leathery, bright green, and glabrous, 4-8 mm long, 0.3-0.5 mm wide, with a thick midvein. The flowering stems are upright, 2-5 cm high, 2-4 small, bract-like pairs of leaves and bear a single flower. The flowers are white with petals 2-2.5 mm long, exceeding the sepals. The purplish sepals are oblong, strongly keeled and with somewhat long hairs at the base. The fruit is a nearly cylindric capsule, opening by 3 valves.

DISTRIBUTION: Map 15. The species is very restricted in its distribution, occuring on serpentine outcrops in western Newfoundland, Mt. Albert (Gaspé Peninsula), Quebec, and Haystack Mt., Vermont.

HABITAT: Serpentine Sandwort is appropriately named as it is found only associated with serpentine outcrops. In Vermont (the single U.S. station) the plant grows on the face of wet serpentine ledges with a northern exposure.

FLOWERING PERIOD: July-August.

ENDANGERMENT: This small station appears to be healthy and in no immediate danger of extirpation since many of the plants occur on inaccessible places on the face of the ledges.

RECOMMENDATIONS: No specific recommendations are needed. However, since this represents the single known station within the United States it would be desirable to have periodic monitoring of the population.

TAXONOMIC COMMENTS:
Synonym: *Arenaria marcescens* Fern.

Serpentine Sandwort belongs to a group of species which have long been recognized in Europe as a distinct genus, *Minuartia*. American botanists have treated the sandworts in a broader sense, all in the genus *Arenaria*. However, McNeill and Levesque have each made a strong case for recognizing *Minuartia*. The European concept is slowly being adopted.

SELECTED REFERENCES: Cook, 1959; Fernald, 1919; House, 1921; Levesque, 1980; McNeill, 1980; Wofford, 1981.

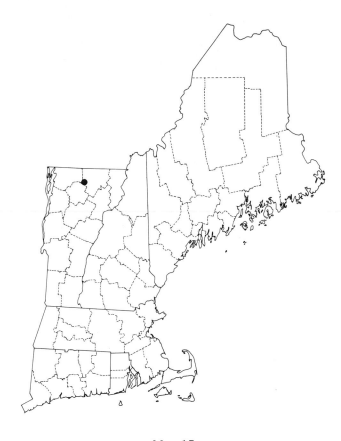

Map 15
Minuartia marcescens

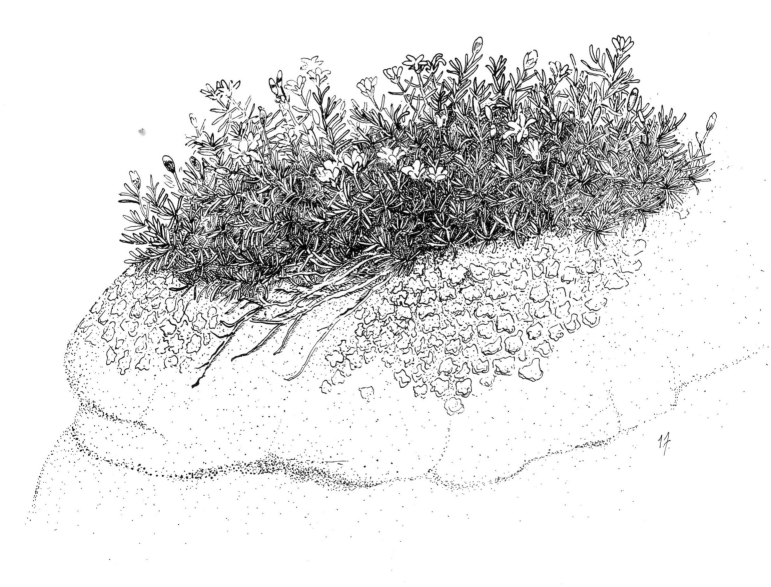

Fig. 15.   Serpentine Sandwort *(Minuartia marcescens)*: Habit X2.

ST. JOHN RIVER LOCO-WEED
Oxytropis campestris (L.) DC.
var. *johannensis* Fern.

STATUS: U.S., 1980 FR Notice of Review
New England Reports: ME

FAMILY: Leguminosae/Fabaceae (Pea or Bean Family)

OTHER NAMES: St. John River Crazy-weed

DISTINCTIVE FEATURES: St. John River Loco-weed is a handsome perennial herb, forming a tufted plant with numerous crowded, short stems emerging from a thick crown or rootstock, and covered with scaley adnate stipules. The leaves (0.5-3 dm long) are pinnately divided, with numerous leaflets which are linear-lanceolate to ovate-lanceolate (8-25 mm long). The stipules are white and membranous, covered with stiffish long hairs when young, loosing them later. The flowers are a rosy color (becoming bluish on drying), borne on scapes 0.5-3.3 dm high, spikes being elongate, several to many flowered (2-11 cm long). The calyx tube is 5-7 mm long with teeth 1.5-3 mm long; the corolla is 1.5-2 cm long. The fruit is a strongly ascending legume (1.5-2 cm long) and the seeds are black, obliquely round to kidney-shaped, as long as broad (1.8-2 mm).

DISTRIBUTION: Map 16. This taxon is endemic to a region of northeastern North America from western Newfoundland and eastern Quebec, south to Nova Scotia and the St. John River Valley of New Brunswick and Maine.

HABITAT: St. John River Loco-weed typically grows in wet calcareous rocks and gravels of sea cliffs and shores.

FLOWERING PERIOD: June-July.

ENDANGERMENT: Destruction of habitat poses the greatest threat to the survival of this plant. Although its range is not as greatly restricted as that of the Furbish Lousewort *(Pedicularis furbishiae)*, many of the sites within the U.S. portion of the range occur in the same area and are therefore threatened by possible hydroelectric projects.

RECOMMENDATIONS: Considerations for protection of this plant should be made in concert with those concerning the Furbish Lousewort.

TAXONOMIC COMMENTS:
Synonyms: *Oxytropis johannensis* (Fern.) Fern.
Aragallus campestris var. *johannensis* (Fern.) Macoun
Aragallus johannensis (Fern.) Heller
Astragalus campestris var. *johannensis* (Fern.) Tidestrom

SELECTED REFERENCES: Barneby, 1952; Fernald, 1899, 1928.

Map 16
Oxytropis campestris var. *johannensis*

Fig. 16.   St. John River Loco-weed (Oxytropis campestris var. *johannensis*): Habit X.9.

PRAIRIE FRINGED ORCHID
Platanthera leucophaea (Nutt.) Lindl.

STATUS: U.S., 1980 FR Notice of Review
New England Reports: ME

FAMILY: Orchidaceae (Orchid Family)

OTHER NAMES: Prairie Orchid, Prairie White-fringe

DISTINCTIVE FEATURES: The Prairie Fringed Orchid is a large, showy, fragrant perennial herb. Its stout, somewhat angled stem grows to a height of 0.2-1.2 m. The leaves are broad and lance-oblong, the larger lower leaves 1.5-3.5 cm broad and 10-20 cm long. The plant produces a large spike-like raceme of large, creamy-white flowers, somewhat loosely arranged (usually 10-20 flowers). The lip of the corolla is divided into 3 broad, wedge-shaped segments which are abundantly fringed. The club-like spur is 2-5 cm long and conspicuously curved outward, exceeding the ovary in length. The fruit is an ellipsoid capsule, 1.8 cm long.

DISTRIBUTION: Map 17. Rare throughout its range, *Platanthera leucophaea* is chiefly a midwestern species of wet prairies of Minnesota and eastern North Dakota, eastern South Dakota, Nebraska, Kansas, Iowa, Missouri, Arkansas, Wisconsin and Illinois; eastward to northern Indiana, Ohio, Michigan, Ontario, Virginia, and New York (probably extinct); disjunct to a single station in Crystal Bog, Crystal, Aroostook Co., Maine.

HABITAT: The single New England station is an open calcareous bog.

FLOWERING PERIOD: Mid-July to mid-August.

ENDANGERMENT: The sole New England population at Crystal Bog has not been seen since 1976. In past years the maximum number of plants observed was twenty. The greatest threats appear to be from groups of wildflower enthusiasts, collecting, and habitat destruction.

RECOMMENDATIONS: Preserve habitat at its present condition and monitor visitations.

TAXONOMIC COMMENTS:
Synonym: *Habenaria leucophaea* (Nutt.) Gray

SELECTED REFERENCES: Ayensu, 1975; Eastman, 1976, 1978; Fernald and Wiegand, 1910; Luer, 1975; Morris and Eames, 1929; Nylander, 1921; Wallace, 1951.

Map 17
Platanthera leucophaea

Fig. 17.   Prairie Fringed Orchid *(Platanthera leucophaea)*: Habit X1; flower X2.

HILL'S PONDWEED
Potamogeton hillii Morong

STATUS: U.S., 1980 FR Notice of Review
New England Reports: VT, MA (add to CT)

FAMILY: Potamogetonaceae (Pondweed Family)

DISTINCTIVE FEATURES: Hill's Pondweed is a submersed aquatic with slender, slightly compressed, heavily ridged stems. The plants bear only submersed leaves which are linear, 3-nerved, 2.0-6.0 cm long, 0.6-2.5 (-4.0) mm wide, ending in a bristle tip (occasionally only apiculate). The midrib is bordered by 1-2 rows of lacunae on each side. The stipules are free, white to light brown and slightly fibrous. The peduncles bearing fruit clusters are slightly club-shaped, recurved and either axillary or terminal. The fruits are drupaceous, 3-keeled 3-4 mm long and ending in a central beak.

DISTRIBUTION: Map 18. *Potamogeton hillii* ranges from western New England and New York to southern Ontario and northern Michigan, south to Pennsylvania and eastern Ohio. Extensive field work in western New England by C. B. Hellquist has shown this species to be more abundant than previously known for the area.

HABITAT: This pondweed grows in highly alkaline ponds and streams.

FRUITING PERIOD: July to late August (fruits essential for identification).

ENDANGERMENT: No threats have been identified in our area. In fact, it is often abundant where it occurs.

RECOMMENDATIONS: Observations on population fluctuations would be valuable.

SELECTED REFERENCES: Fernald, 1932; Haynes, 1974; Hellquist and Crow, 1980.

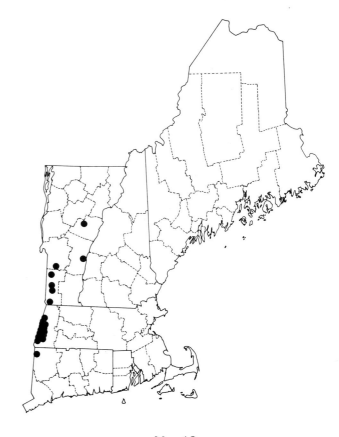

Map 18
Potamogeton hillii

36

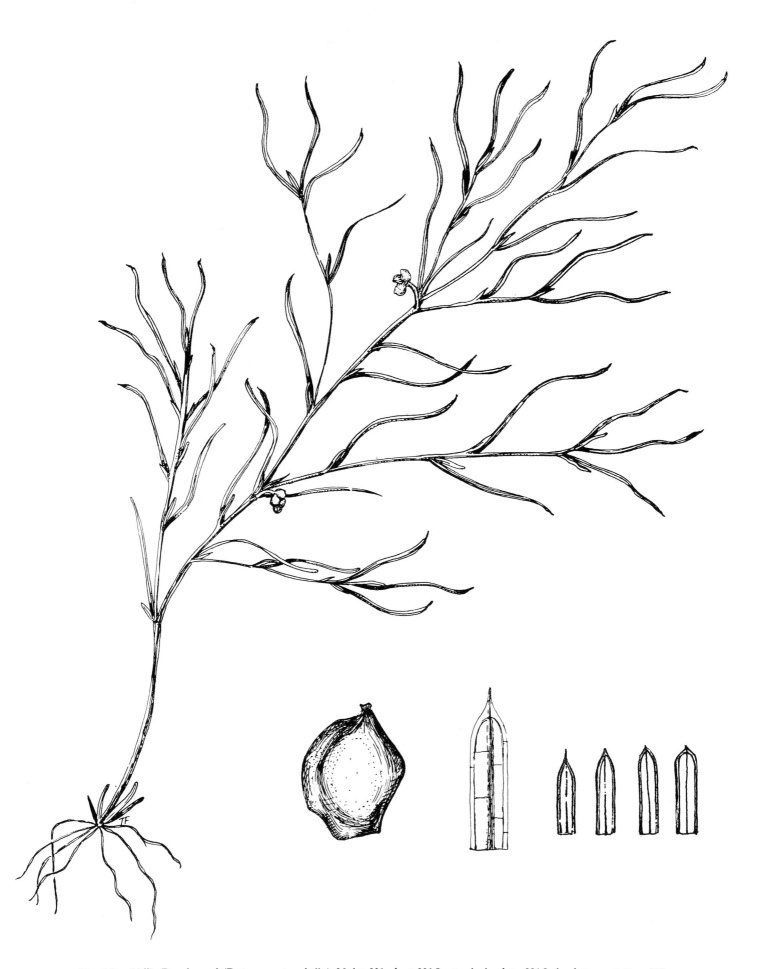

Fig. 18.   Hill's Pondweed *(Potamogeton hillii)*: Habit X1; fruit X10; single leaf tip X10; leaf tip variation X2.

ONE-SIDED PONDWEED
Potamogeton lateralis Morong

STATUS: U.S., 1980 FR Notice of Review
New England Reports: NH, VT, MA, CT

FAMILY: Potamogetonaceae (Pondweed Family)

DISTINCTIVE FEATURES: One-sided Pondweed is a submersed aquatic with much branched slender, thread-like stems. Plants may bear both floating and submersed leaves or only submersed leaves. The floating leaves are small, 0.6-1.5 cm long and 0.4-1 mm wide, often opposite in 1-3 pairs; blades with 5-7 veins, usually spatulate. The submersed leaves are narrowly linear, acute, 1.5-6 cm long and 0.4-1.0 mm wide, and have a prominent midrib. The stipules are completely free, delicate, many-nerved, about 5 mm long, falling off with age. The fruits are small and drupaceous, obliquely obovoid, slightly compressed with a strongly rounded back. Fruits develop only on plants bearing submersed leaves; floating leaved plants, although sometimes bearing flowers, remain sterile.

DISTRIBUTION: Map 19. *Potamogeton lateralis* is extremely rare, reported from widely scattered locations in New England, New York (possibly extinct), Michigan and eastern Minnesota. In New England only the New Hampshire and Vermont stations have been documented since 1980. One new station was discovered in Vermont in 1979 by W. D. Countryman.

HABITAT: Quiet waters.

FRUITING PERIOD: July to late August (fruits essential for identification).

ENDANGERMENT: Although no specific threats have been identified, this pondweed is extremely rare throughout its range. Massachusetts, Connecticut, and New York populations appear to be extinct.

RECOMMENDATIONS: Populations should be monitored.

TAXONOMIC COMMENTS: Misdeterminations of specimens may occur because of similarities to *Potamogeton vaseyi* and *P. pusillus* var. *tenuissimus*. The taxonomic status is questionable and may be better treated as a synonym under *P. vaseyi*.

SELECTED REFERENCES: Fernald, 1932; Hellquist and Crow, 1980; Mitchell *et al.*, 1980.

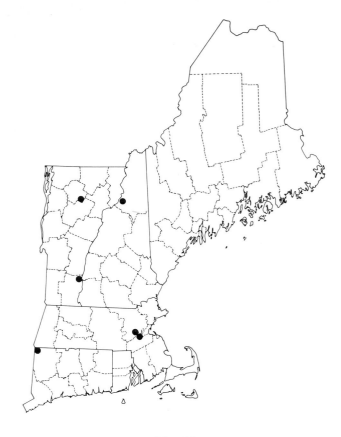

Map 19
Potamogeton lateralis

Fig. 19.   One-sided Pondweed *(Potamogeton lateralis)*: Habit X1; upper portion showing floating leaves X2; leaf tip X10; fruit X10.

BOOTT'S RATTLESNAKE-ROOT
Prenanthes boottii (DC.) Gray

STATUS: U.S., 1980 FR Notice of Review
New England Reports: ME, NH, VT

FAMILY: Compositae/Asteraceae (Aster or Sunflower Family)

DISTINCTIVE FEATURES: Boott's Rattlesnake-root is a high elevation perennial herb with an erect, unbranched stem reaching 10-30 cm in height. Although there is considerable variability in leaf shape, the lowest leaves tend to be triangular or heart-shaped at the base of the blade; middle leaves are somewhat oblong and upper leaves become lance-shaped, tapering to a short petiole. The flowering stalk is somewhat simple, bearing flower heads which contain 10-18 flowers and are subtended by a bell-shaped whorl of 10-15 primary bracts. Flower heads are erect to spreading and some nodding. *Prenanthes trifoliolata* var. *nana*, which also occurs above timberline, differs in having basal leaves which are often deeply cleft, forming 3 conspicuous lobes and flowers subtended by 6-8 primary bracts. *Prenanthes altissima*, a lowland species which occasionally occurs above timberline, is a taller species. Its basal leaves are also deeply 3-lobed and has only 5-6 flowers subtended by 5 primary bracts. Flowers are important in the identification of specimens.

DISTRIBUTION: Map 20. *Prenanthes boottii* has a very restricted overall distribution, known only from alpine regions of Maine, New Hampshire, Vermont and northern New York. Most of the sites occur in New Hampshire, being somewhat frequent throughout the alpine region of the Presidential and Franconia Ranges. Three sites are known in Maine, two sites in Vermont and two mountain peaks in New York.

HABITAT: The plant grows in moist alpine meadows and stream-sides and in cold, open subalpine ravines.

FLOWERING PERIOD: Flowers are produced late in the season, generally from late July through August, producing seed in late August to September. It appears to reproduce primarily by seed.

ENDANGERMENT: Boott's Rattlesnake-root grows in a very fragile environment. The species does not appear to be in immediate danger of extinction, however, since its occurrence is infrequent within the alpine zone particular care should be exercised in trail repair work.

RECOMMENDATIONS: Due to its overall restricted geographical range and general rarity, populations should be periodically monitored to determine fluctuations in population size and to identify any adverse impacts.

TAXONOMIC COMMENTS:
Synonym: *Nabalus boottii* DC.

This synonym appears in *Britton and Brown Illustrated Flora of the Northeastern United States and Adjacent Canada*, 2nd edition, which has been reprinted by Dover Publications, sometimes mistaken for a more recent edition than the 3rd edition, which is still in print.

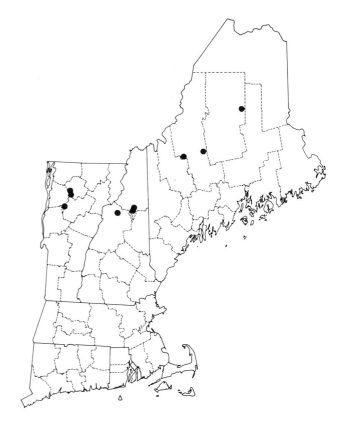

Map 20
Prenanthes boottii

SELECTED REFERENCES: Gleason, 1952; Mitchell *et al.*, 1980; Storks and Crow, 1979.

Fig. 20.   Boott's Rattlesnake-root *(Prenanthes boottii)*: Habit X1; head of flowers X3.

GRAVES BEACH PLUM
Prunus maritima Marshall
var. *gravesii* (Small) Anderson

STATUS: U.S., 1980 FR Notice of Review
New England Reports: CT

FAMILY: Rosaceae (Rose Family)

DISTINCTIVE FEATURES: Graves Beach Plum is a low, slender, branching shrub reaching about 2 m in height. Resembling the common Beach Plum *Prunus maritima* var. *maritima*, it is particularly distinguished by its nearly round leaves (orbicular), in contrast to the elliptical leaves of the common Beach Plum. Four characters, seed size, style length, leaf length, and leaf length/width ratio, have been shown to be significantly distinct (statistically) for Graves Beach Plum, however, the whole range of variability of even these characters overlap with Beach Plum to some degree.

DISTRIBUTION: Map 21. Graves Beach Plum is known from only a single station along the shore of Long Island Sound in southeastern Connecticut.

HABITAT: The shrub grows on a gravelly sand ridge in low shrubby thickets with associated coastal shrubs including Beach Plum *(Prunus maritima* var. *maritima)*, Wild Cherry *(Prunus serotina)*, Honeysuckle *(Lonicera japonica)*, Virginia Creeper *(Parthenocissus quinquefolia)*, Poison Ivy *(Toxicodendron radicans)*, and Bittersweet *(Celastrus orbiculatus)*.

FLOWERING PERIOD: Late May to early June.

ENDANGERMENT: The population appears to be represented by a single plant which produces additional upright stems from underground runners. The seeds are fertile, but no seedling establishment has been found. The chief threat comes from bathers at the adjacent beach unknowingly trampling the plant.

RECOMMENDATIONS: The snow-fencing has proved inadequate to prevent people from short-cutting through the area. Stonger fencing must be maintained to protect the population. An educational sign would also be appropriate.

TAXONOMIC COMMENTS:
Synonym: *Prunus gravesii* Small

A change in the taxonomic status of this plant has recently been made after careful study of the population biology of Graves Beach Plum by Dr. G. J. Anderson, University of Connecticut. He concludes that this plant is a mutant derivitive of *Prunus maritima* and that since the flowers are self-incompatible, it must rely on Beach Plum as a pollen source for seed production.

SELECTED REFERENCES: Anderson, 1980, 1980a; Mehrhoff, 1978; Small, 1897.

Map 21
Prunus maritima var. *gravesii*

Fig. 21. Graves Beach Plum *(Prunus maritima* var. *gravesii)*: Habit, flowering and vegetative branches X1.

AMERICAN CHAFFSEED
Schwalbea americana L.

STATUS: U.S., 1980 FR Notice of Review
New England Reports: MA, CT

FAMILY: Scrophulariaceae (Figwort or Snapdragon
Family)

DISTINCTIVE FEATURES: American Chaffseed is a finely pubescent perennial herb, reaching 3-8 dm tall; the pubescence consisting of recurved hairs. The leaves are alternate, sessile, elliptical-lanceolate, 2-5 cm long and rarely over 1 cm wide, conspicuously 3-veined; the leaves becoming progressively smaller upward. The flowers are solitary in the axils of the uppermost leaves, forming a leafy spike-like raceme. The calyx is about 2 cm long, with anterior lobes obtuse. The corolla is pale yellowish, purple to purplish distally, 3-3.5 cm long. The fruit is a capsule, 10-12 mm long and enclosed within a calyx with 12 strongly projecting ribs.

DISTRIBUTION: Map 22. *Schwalbea americana*, in the strict sense, has been reported from the Coastal Plain of Massachusetts and Connecticut and the sand plains near Albany, New York south along the Coastal Plain to northern Virginia.

HABITAT: The plant is typically found growing in moist sandy acidic soil, especially in pine barrens.

FLOWERING PERIOD: June to mid-July.

ENDANGERMENT: Development in coastal areas appears to be the major threat to populations. Virginia, Delaware, Maryland and New York all report this species to have been extirpated! New Jersey confirms only one extant site where it is vulnerable to development. In Connecticut the most recent report of the species is 1913, a locality which has undergone considerable modification. Of the nine historical sites in Massachusetts only one, a dry bog in Siasconset on Nantucket Island, has been documented recently (1961, specimen collected by F. C. McKeever); Coddington and Field state that it was last verified in the state in 1967.

RECOMMENDATIONS: Additional field work is needed to assess the existence and present status of populations.

TAXONOMIC COMMENTS: This report has adopted Pennell's concept of the species. Fernald and Gleason each regard the species in a broader sense, including *Schwalbea australis* Pennell (Coastal Plain from North Carolina to Florida and Louisiana; inland on the Cumberland Plateau of eastern Tennessee and southeastern Kentucky).

SELECTED REFERENCES: Broome *et al.*, 1979; Coddington and Field, 1978; Fernald, 1950; Gleason, 1952; Mehrhoff, 1978; Mitchell *et al.*, 1980; Pennell, 1935; Porter, 1979; Snyder and Vivian, 1981; Tucker *et al.*, 1979.

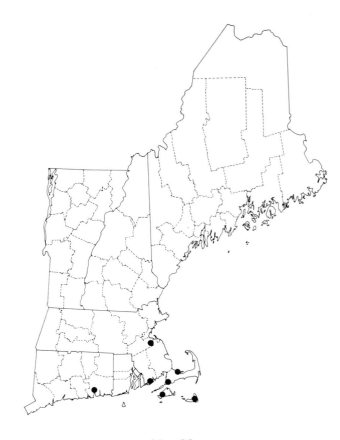

Map 22
Schwalbea americana

Fig. 22.   American Chaffseed *(Schwalbea americana)*: Habit X1; flower X3.

BARBED-BRISTLE BULRUSH
Scirpus ancistrochaetus Schuyler

STATUS: U.S., 1980 FR Notice of Review
New England Reports: VT, MA

FAMILY: Cyperaceae (Sedge Family)

OTHER NAMES: Fish-hook Bulrush, Northeastern Bulrush

DISTINCTIVE FEATURES: Barbed-bristle Bulrush is a tall, leafy bulrush. A perennial, flowering stems are produced from a short, almost woody, underground rhizome and grow to 0.8-1.2 m tall. The rays of the inflorescence are characteristically arching, thus the plant is distinctive in the field. The clusters of spikelets are subtended by involucral leaves, the lowermost 3-5 mm wide and 5.5-17 cm long. The scales of the brown spikelets are slightly mucronate, 1.5-1.9 mm long (central portion of spikelet). The flowers have 6 perianth bristles which are 1.1-1.7 mm long, rigid, armed with thick-walled, sharp-pointed, downward facing barbs. The stamens vary from 0-3 and the styles are 3-parted, up to 1.35 mm long. The fruits, achenes, are yellow-brown, 1.1-1.35 mm long and are distinctly thickened and tough at the top (above the locule) in contrast to other species which have a soft, thin wall.

The species is most similar to *Scirpus atrovirens* which has narrower leaves and flowers with bristles that are less rigid, often delicate and wrinkled, with thin-walled, round-tipped barbs; the achenes are also shorter, about 1 mm.

DISTRIBUTION Map 23. A relatively newly known species (described in 1962), Barbed-bristle Bulrush has been reported from Virginia, Pennsylvania, New York, Massachusetts, and Vermont.

HABITAT: Bogs, swales and shores of acidic or slightly alkaline ponds.

FLOWERING PERIOD: Mid-June to July; fruiting July to September.

ENDANGERMENT: The typical sites of this plant are subject to drainage for development purposes. New York reports that the species is believed extirpated in that state and several localities with the plant have been lost in Pennsylvania.

RECOMMENDATIONS: Monitor known populations.

SELECTED REFERENCES: Coddington and Field, 1978; Countryman, 1978; Mitchell *et al.*, 1980; Porter, 1979; Schuyler, 1962, 1967; Wiegman, 1979.

Map 23
Scirpus ancistrochaetus

Fig. 23.   Barbed-bristle Bulrush *(Scirpus ancistrochaetus)*: Habit X1; spikelet X4; scale of spikelet X20; achene with barbed-bristles X20; barbed-bristle X40.

LONG'S BULRUSH
Scirpus longii Fern.

STATUS: U.S., 1980 FR Notice of Review
New England Reports: ME, MA, CT

FAMILY: Cyperaceae (Sedge Family)

DISTINCTIVE FEATURES: Long's Bulrush is a robust, leafy bulrush. A perennial, the plant produces tall flowering stems from thick, elongated rhizomes, stems reaching 9-14 dm high. The leaves are green to slightly glaucous, 3-8 mm wide, serrate along the margins and keel. The long pedicelled spikelets are subtended by 2-3 involucral leaves, blackish at the base and glutinous, shorter than or about equaling the umbel. The spikelets are broadly ovate to elliptic, 2-5 mm wide and usually elongating more than 1 cm. The scales are blackish, mostly 2.2-3.1 mm long, elliptic or narrowly elliptic to obovate or narrowly obovate. The flowers have 6 whitish perianth bristles, long and contorted, with smooth margins, exceeding the scales at maturity. The achenes are reddish-brown, elliptic or obovate, 0.7-1 mm long, but few reach maturity.

DISTRIBUTION: Map 24. *Scirpus longii* grows in marshes near the Atlantic Coast in widely scattered locations from western Nova Scotia (one site) to southern New Jersey. The report from North Carolina was based on a misidentified specimen according to Schuyler.

HABITAT: Marshes near the coast. A large portion of the herbarium specimens have charred leaves, and Schuyler suggests that fire may be an important factor in stimulating flowering.

FLOWERING PERIOD: May-June; fruits maturing in late June.

ENDANGERMENT: Alteration of habitat and development appear to pose the greatest threats to survival. In Connecticut recent field work has failed to relocate that state's single population of *Scirpus longii*, and heavy industrial development in the area of the site suggests that it may have been extirpated. In Massachusetts six historical sites are known, most of which are in the greater Boston area where many formerly rich wetland areas have been destroyed for development. Field work has failed to relocate Long's Bulrush at any of the sites.

While Nova Scotia lists the species among its rare plants (a single northernmost site), the New Jersey report on rare and endangered plants comments that the species is locally abundant and presently not viewed as threatened with extinction.

RECOMMENDATIONS: None.

TAXONOMIC COMMENTS: There appears to be no question of taxonomic status for *Scirpus longii*. The species is closely related to *S. cyperinus* and Schuyler has reported hybrids between the two species along the Charles River in Dedham, Massachusetts and in New Jersey. (However, *S. longii* was not found growing with the hybrids.)

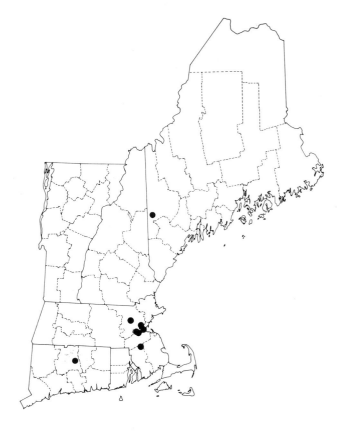

Map 24
Scirpus longii

SELECTED REFERENCES: Fernald, 1911; Schuyler, 1963, 1964, 1967.

Fig. 24.   Long's Bulrush *(Scirpus longii)*: Habit X1; achene with bristles X10; leaf segment showing serrate keel and margins X10; scale of spikelet X10; spikelet X4.

SPREADING GLOBE-FLOWER
Trollius laxus Salisb.
subsp. *laxus*

STATUS: U.S., 1980 FR Notice of Review
New England Reports: CT

FAMILY: Ranunculaceae (Buttercup Family)

DISTINCTIVE FEATURES: Spreading Globe-flower bears a general resemblance to our common buttercups and can therefore be easily overlooked. It is a smooth perennial herb with a large solitary, terminal, greenish-yellow flower. The leaves are palmately parted into 5-7 segments; basal leaves with long petioles and 1-3 stem leaves with very short or no petioles, occurring mostly above the middle of the stem. The flowers have 5-6 pale greenish-yellow spreading sepals and 15-25 inconspicuous petals. Several to many follicles develop from a single flower, approximately 1 cm long and transversely veined.

DISTRIBUTION: Map 25. The plant is rare and local from western Connecticut to New York, south to New Jersey, Pennsylvania, and Ohio. Old reports for New Hampshire and Maine are erroneous. In New England four historical records are documented, all in Litchfield County, Connecticut.

HABITAT: The Spreading Globe-flower grows in rich meadows and swamps, particularly associated with limestone areas in Connecticut.

FLOWERING PERIOD: Late April to early May.

ENDANGERMENT: The chief threat to survival appears to be destruction of habitat due to development at two of the three known New England sites.

RECOMMENDATIONS: Additional field work is needed for this species. Preservation of habitat and protection from collecting are required for survival of native populations, although the species is readily propagated by seed for ornamental purposes.

TAXONOMIC COMMENTS:
Synonym: *Trollius laxus* Salisb. var. *laxus*

The western taxon has recently been elevated to subspecific rank, *T. laxus* subsp. *albiflorus* (A. Gray) Löve, Löve, and Kapoor; thus the eastern taxon is currently recognized at that rank also.

SELECTED REFERENCES: Eastman, 1980; Fernald *et al.*, 1919; Löve *et al.*, 1971; Mehrhoff, 1978; Mitchell *et al.*, 1980; Tucker *et al.*, 1979; Wiegman, 1979.

Map 25
Trollius laxus subsp. *laxus*

Fig. 25.   Spreading Globe-flower *(Trollius laxus* subsp. *laxus)* Habit X1.

MARSH VALERIAN
Valeriana uliginosa (T. and G.) Rydb.

STATUS: U.S., 1980 FR Notice of Review
New England Reports: ME, VT, (add to NH)

FAMILY: Valerianaceae (Valerian Family)

OTHER NAMES: Swamp Valerian, Northern Valerian

DISTINCTIVE FEATURES: Marsh Valerian is a tall perennial herb, reaching 0.3-1 m in height. The basal rosette leaves are simple or cleft, the larger leaves 5-15 cm long and 2.8 cm broad. The larger stem leaves are compound, 3-6 pairs, 6-16 cm long and 5-10 cm broad, with leaflets 0.4-1.6 cm broad. The flowers are borne in a somewhat flat-topped (corymbose) inflorescence 3-15 cm across, which becomes elongated as the fruits develop. The flowers are white, the corolla tubular, with a slight protuberance on one side toward the base, 5-7 mm long. The calyx teeth are modified into plumose bristles, rolled up in flower. The bractlets subtending the flower are ciliate when young. The fruits are 1-seeded, 1-locular.

DISTRIBUTION: Map 26. Marsh Valerian grows from Quebec and New Brunswick to western Ontario, south to northern New England, Michigan, and Wisconsin.

HABITAT: The plants typically grow in calcareous swamps and bogs, and wet woods.

FLOWERING PERIOD: Late May-June.

ENDANGERMENT: The plant is considered rare throughout its range. Only five New England sites are confirmed extant, however no specific threats are presently known.

RECOMMENDATIONS: Extant sites should be monitored.

SELECTED REFERENCES: Fernald, 1950; Gleason, 1952.

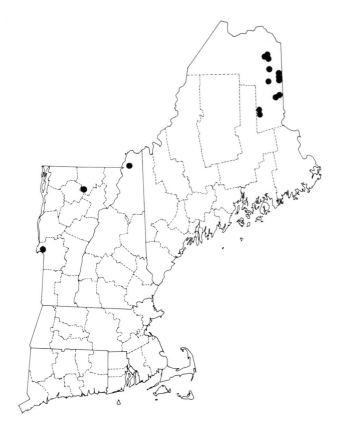

Map 26
Valeriana uliginosa

Fig. 26.   Marsh Valerian *(Valeriana uliginosa)*: Habit X.9; flower X4.

NEW ENGLAND VIOLET
Viola novae-angliae House

STATUS: U.S., 1980 FR Notice of Review
New England Reports: (add to ME)

FAMILY: Violaceae (Violet Family)

DISTINCTIVE FEATURES: A stemless violet, New England Violet is a perennial herb with leaves arising from a stout, ascending rhizome. The leaf blades tend to be small and somewhat triangular (3.5-7 cm long and 2-5 cm broad), with only 6-12 teeth along each side (sometimes appearing to lack teeth), and minutely pubescent. The flowers are violet-purple, all 5 petals have long soft hairs (villous). The fruit is a globose capsule, mottled with purple. The seeds are plump, light brown to buff.

DISTRIBUTION: Map 27. A northern species originally described from Maine, *Viola novae-angliae* ranges from the Lake Superior region of Minnesota, Wisconsin, Michigan, and western Ontario and eastern Manitoba; disjunct to New Brunswick and northern Maine.

HABITAT: Gravelly and sandy shores, wet ledges, and meadows.

FLOWERING PERIOD: Late May and June.

ENDANGERMENT: Although *Viola novae-angliae* is rare throughout its range, no specific threats are known. A vigorous population occurs along the Allagash River in northern Maine.

RECOMMENDATIONS: Populations should be periodically monitored.

TAXONOMIC COMMENTS: Russell notes that in Minnesota and Wisconsin the species grades into *Viola sagittata* and that the two species are difficult to separate.

SELECTED REFERENCES: Fernald, 1950; Gleason, 1952; Russell, 1965; Scoggan, 1978.

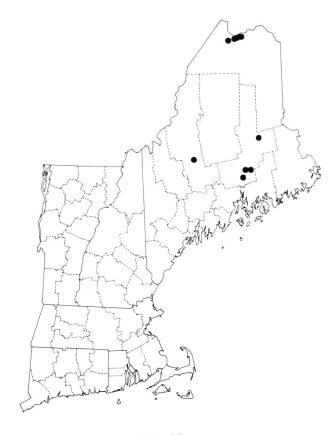

Map 27
Viola novae-angliae

Fig. 27.   New England Violet *(Viola novae-angliae)*: Habit X1; flower X3.

Pedicularis furbishiae

Photo by: Susan Gawler

Photo by: Raymond Graber

Potentilla robbinsiana

Isotria medeoloides

Photo by: David Snyder

Paronychia argyrocoma var. albimontana

Helianthemum dumosum

Photo by: Irene Stuckey

Minuartia marcescens

Oxytropis campestris var. johannensis

Platanthera leucophaea

Photo by: Charles Sheviak

Schwalbea americana

Trollius laxus subsp. *laxus*

Valeriana uliginosa

Photo by: Susan Gawler

Viola novae-angliae

Photo by: Susan Gawler

New England Rare Taxa of National Significance

FERNS and FERN ALLIES

OPHIOGLOSSACEAE (Adder's-tongue Family)

Botrychium lunaria (L.) Sw. (Moonwort). Fig. 28. Map 28. Occurs in gravelly sites at edge of spruce woods, stream margins, meadows and open rocky woodlands. Chiefly a species of western North America; disjunct in eastern North America.

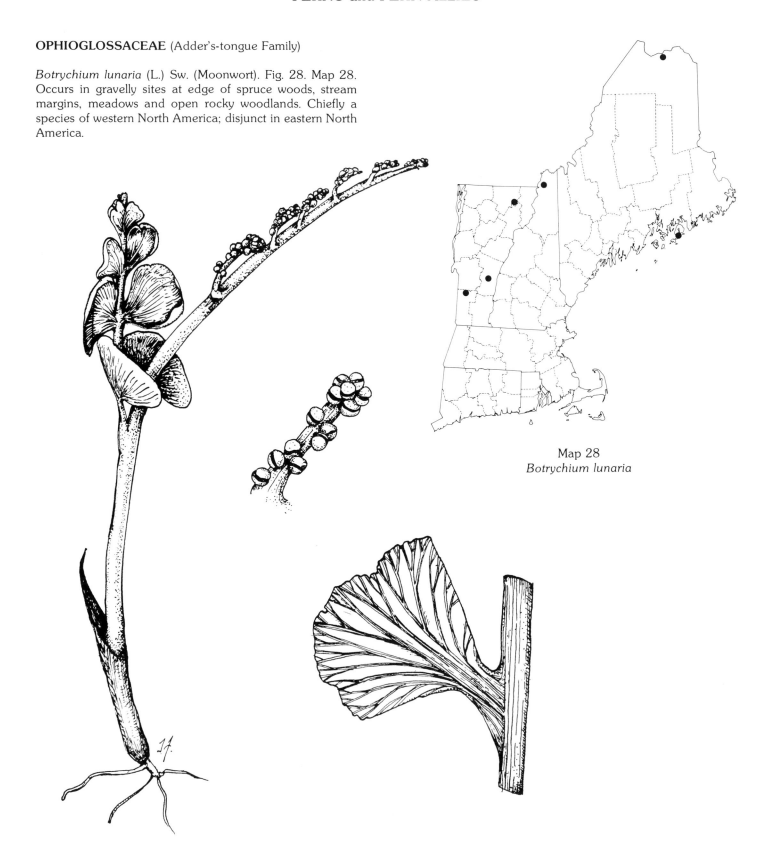

Map 28
Botrychium lunaria

Fig. 28.   Moonwort *(Botrychium lunaria)*: Habit X2; cluster of sporangia X5; portion of frond showing vein pattern X3.

POLYPODIACEAE (Fern Family)

Asplenium viride Huds. (Green Spleenwort). Fig. 29. Map 29.
A plant of shaded sites, growing in crevices of limestone rocks
and ledges in Vermont; along shaded streams on serpentine
outcrops in Maine. Circumboreal distribution.

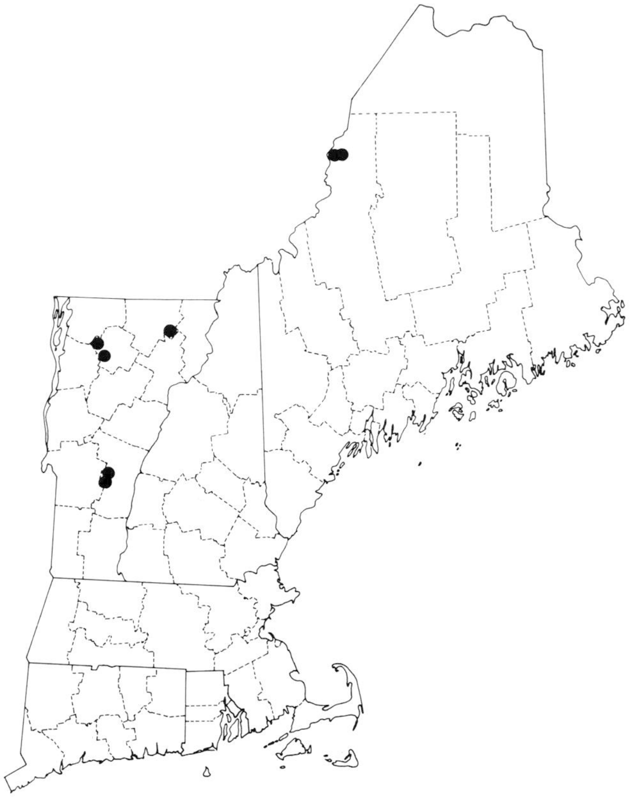

Map 29
Asplenium viride

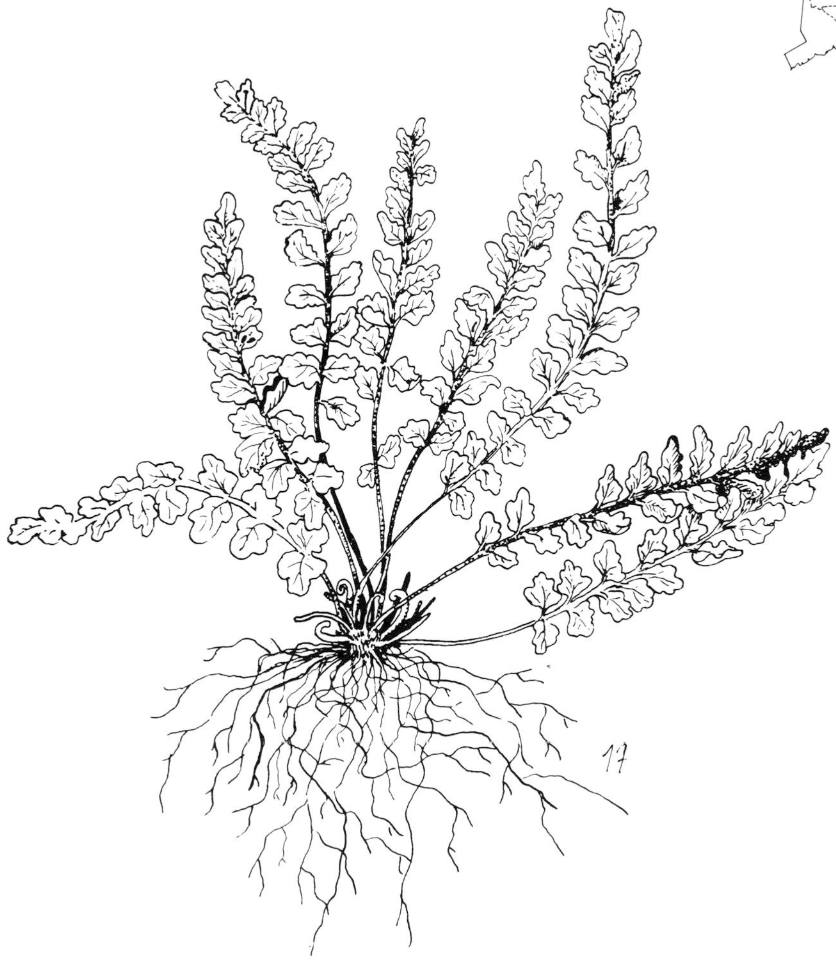

Fig. 29.   Green Spleenwort *(Asplenium viride)*: Habit X1; portion of frond showing sori X3.

57

Drypoteris filix-mas (L.) Schott (Male Fern). Fig. 30. Map 30. A plant of calcareous sites of rich rocky woods, glades, ravines, and rocky slopes. Circumboreal distribution.

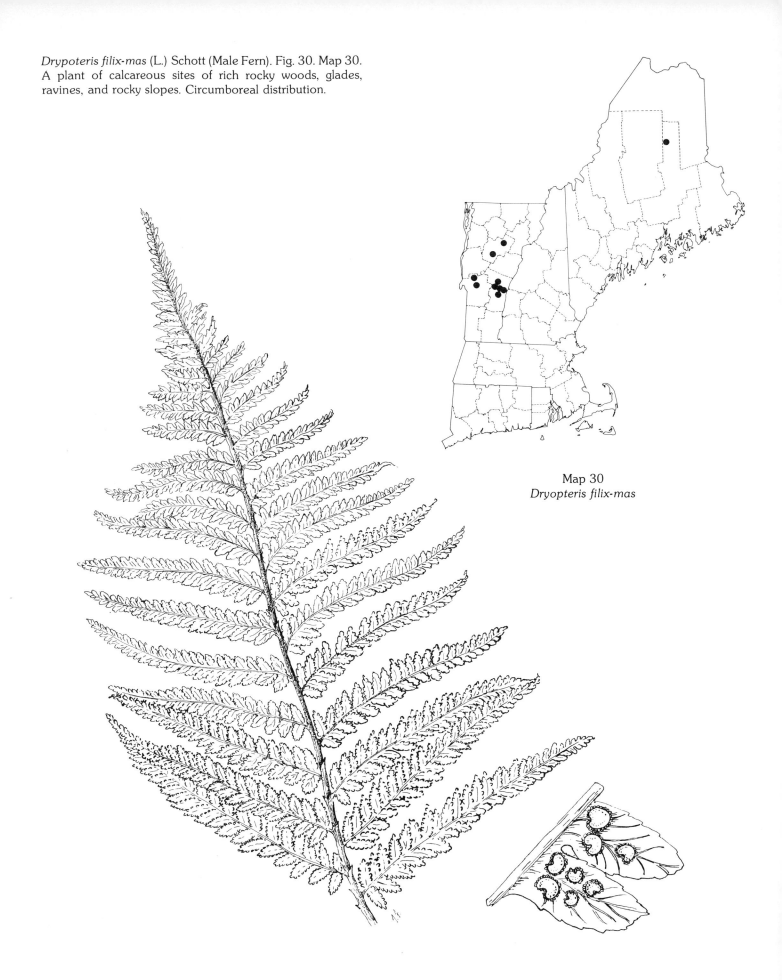

Map 30
Dryopteris filix-mas

Fig. 30.   Male Fern *(Dryopteris filix-mas)*:   Frond X.7; portion of frond showing sori X4.

Woodsia alpina (Bolton) S. F. Gray (Northern Woodsia). Fig. 31. Map 31. Grows chiefly on cool, moist limestone cliffs and ledges in northern New England. Widely scattered in arctic regions, circumpolar distribution; disjunct to northern New England.

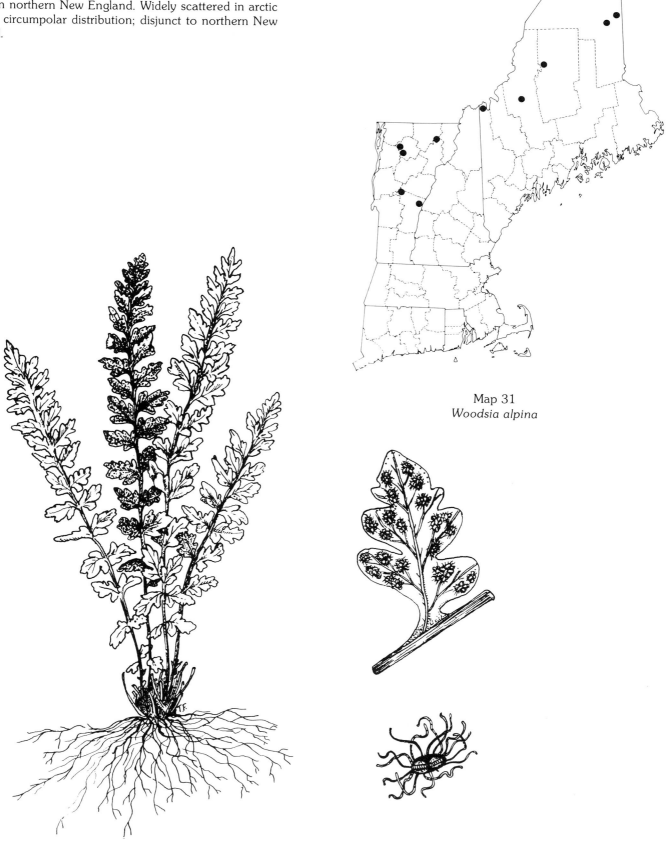

Map 31
Woodsia alpina

Fig. 31. Northern Woodsia *(Woodsia alpina):* Habit X1; portion of frond showing sori X3; detail of sorus showing filamentous segments of indusium X12.

Woodsia glabella R. Br. (Smooth Woodsia).   Fig. 32. Map 32. Occurring chiefly on shaded, moist, calcareous rocks of ledges and cliffs in northern New England. Wide-ranging arctic-alpine species, circumpolar distribution.

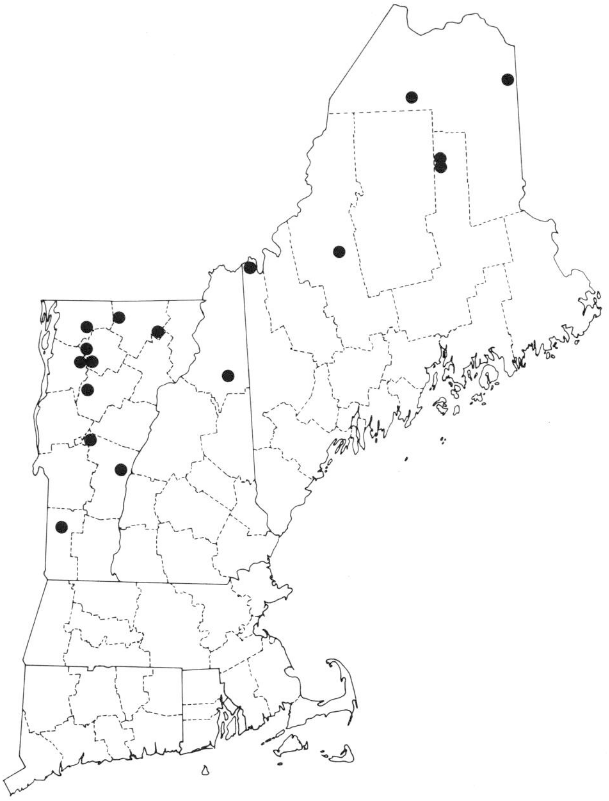

Map 32
Woodsia glabella

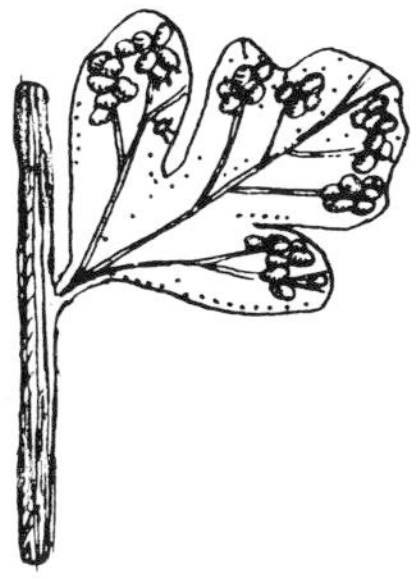

Fig. 32.   Smooth Woodsia *(Woodsia glabella)*:   Habit X1; portion of frond showing paired pinnae X2; single pinna showing sori X5.

SCHIZAEACEAE

Lygodium palmatum (Bernh.) Sw. (Climbing Fern). Fig. 33.
Map 33. Moist woods and thickets in acid soil. Georgia and
Tennessee, northward chiefly in the mountains, to New
England; widely scattered colonies throughout its range.

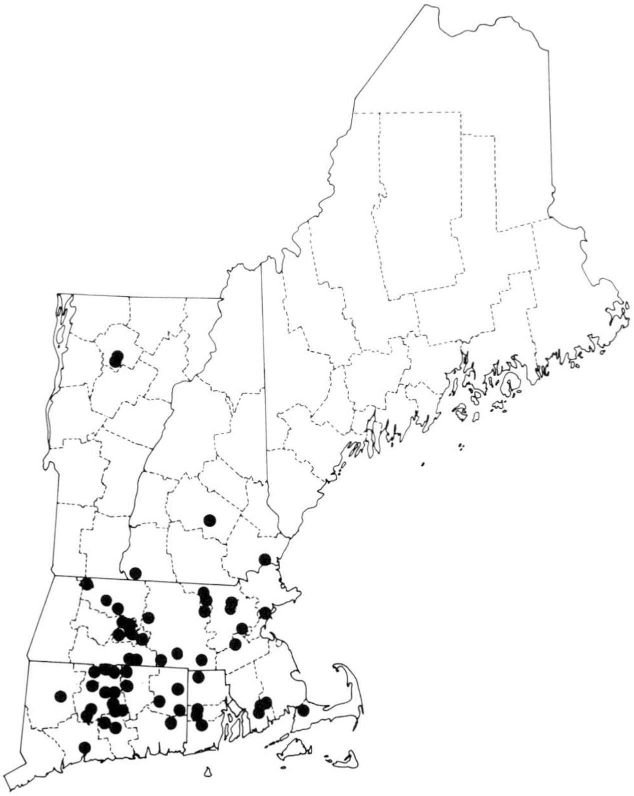

Map 33
Lygodium palmatum

Fig. 33. Climbing Fern *(Lygodium palmatum):* Habit X1; sterile pinna showing vein pattern X1; fertile pinna showing sori X3.

SELAGINELLACEAE (Spike-moss Family)

Selaginella selaginoides (L.) Link (Spike-moss). Fig. 34. Map 34. Two New England sites, a sphagnum bog and a mossy, springy river margin in northern Maine. Circumboreal distribution.

Map 34
Selaginella selaginoides

Fig. 34.   Spike-moss *(Selaginella selaginoides)*:   Habit X1; fertile leaf showing sporangium X10.

MONOCOTS

ALISMATACEAE (Water-plantain Family)

Echinodorus tenellus (Mart.) Buchenau var. *parvulus* (Engelmann) Fassett (Dwarf Burhead). Map 35. Now believed extirpated in New England. Historically known from four sites in eastern Massachusetts, growing on sandy shores of ponds. Occurs very locally from Massachusetts west to southern Ontario and Minnesota, south to central Florida and southern Texas, chiefly on the Coastal Plain. (synonym: *E. parvulus* Engelmann)

Map 35
Echinodorus tenellus var. *parvulus*

Sagittaria teres S. Wats. (Quill-leaved Arrowhead). Fig. 35. Map 36. Common locally in sandy acid Coastal Plain fresh water ponds of southeastern Massachusetts, rare inland in Massachusetts and Rhode Island. A Coastal Plain species from southern Massachusetts south to southern New Jersey; apparently extirpated in Delaware and Maryland. Carolina populations now regarded as *S. isoetiformis*.

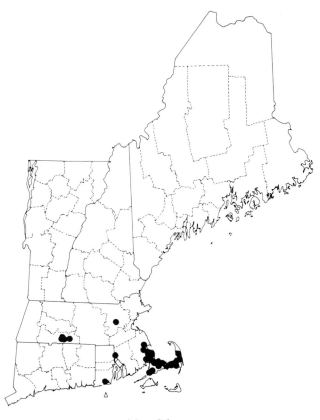

Map 36
Sagittaria teres

63

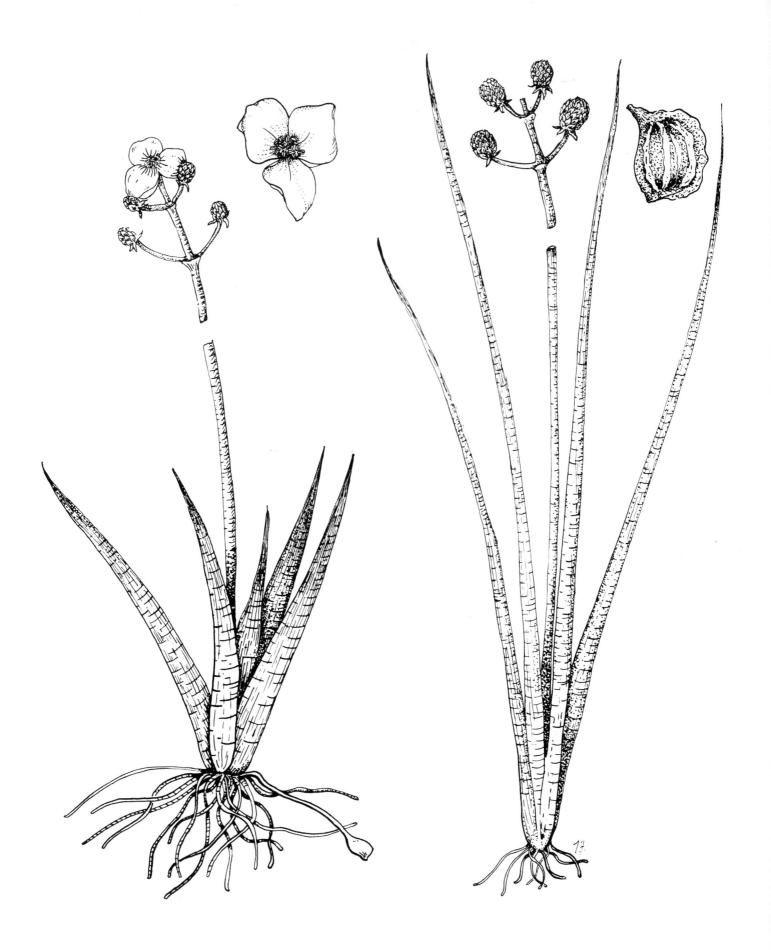

Fig. 35.   Quill-leaved Arrowhead *(Sagittaria teres)*: Habits showing extremes in leaf variation X1; flower X2; fruiting branch X2; achene X10.

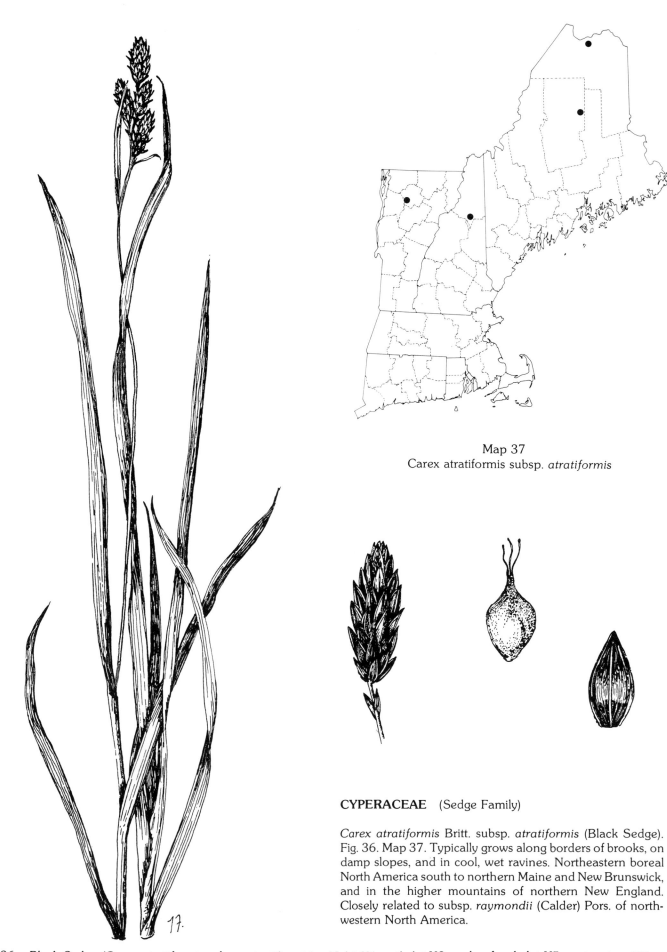

Map 37
Carex atratiformis subsp. *atratiformis*

CYPERACEAE   (Sedge Family)

Carex atratiformis Britt. subsp. *atratiformis* (Black Sedge).
Fig. 36. Map 37. Typically grows along borders of brooks, on
damp slopes, and in cool, wet ravines. Northeastern boreal
North America south to northern Maine and New Brunswick,
and in the higher mountains of northern New England.
Closely related to subsp. *raymondii* (Calder) Pors. of northwestern North America.

Fig. 36.   Black Sedge *(Carex atratiformis* subsp. *atratiformis)*:   Habit X1; spikelet X3; scale of spikelet X5; perigynium X5.

Carex capitata L. var. *arctogena* (H. Smith) Hult. (Capitate Sedge). Map 38. Occurs in peaty alpine meadows of two mountains in New Hampshire. Low arctic, amphi-Atlantic distribution. This taxon is treated by some authors as *C. arctogena*.

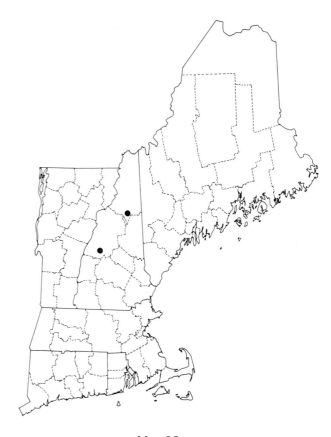

Map 38
Carex capitata var. *arctogena*

Carex flava L. var. *gaspensis* Fern. (Gaspé Sedge). Map 39. A plant of calcareous springs and shores; three northern New England sites. A restricted distribution, from Newfoundland and Anticosti Island to Lake Mistassini, Quebec, south to northeastern Maine and northern Vermont.

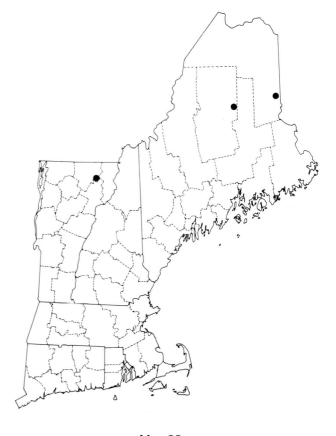

Map 39
Carex flava var. *gaspensis*

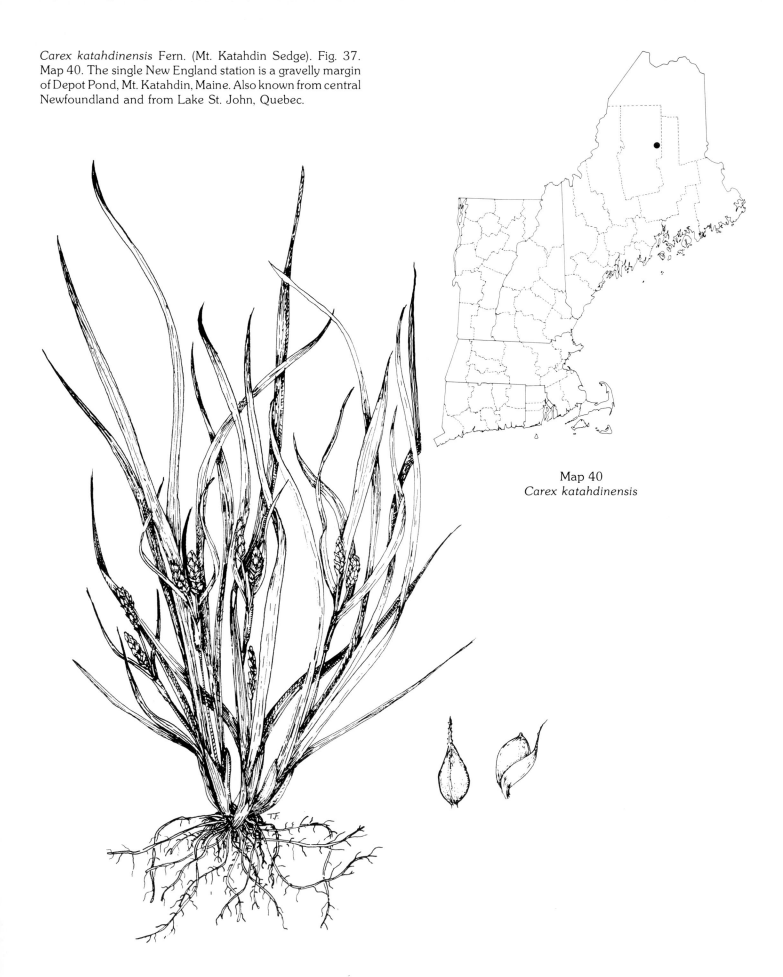

Carex katahdinensis Fern. (Mt. Katahdin Sedge). Fig. 37. Map 40. The single New England station is a gravelly margin of Depot Pond, Mt. Katahdin, Maine. Also known from central Newfoundland and from Lake St. John, Quebec.

Map 40
Carex katahdinensis

Fig. 37. Mt. Katahdin Sedge *(Carex katahdinensis)*: Habit X1; scale of spikelet X5; perigynium with scale X5.

Carex lenticularis Michx. var. *albimontana* Dew. (White Mountain Sedge) Map 41. Occurs in cool, wet ravines on Mt. Washington, New Hampshire. Ranges from northern Labrador to Newfoundland and the Gaspé Peninsula; disjunct to New Hampshire.

Map 41
Carex lenticularis var. *albimontana*

Carex richardsonii R. Br. (Richardson's Sedge) Map 42. Known in New England only from a dry limestone site on Mt. Equinox, Vermont. Distributed from southwestern Vermont to northern Alberta south to western New York, northern Ohio, northern Indiana, northern Illinois, Minnesota, and South Dakota; very rare in the eastern portion of the range.

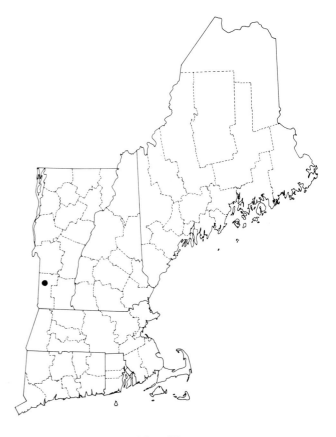

Map 42
Carex richardsonii

Rhynchospora inundata (Oakes) Fern. (Horned-rush). Fig. 38. Map 43. Margins of shallow ponds in southeastern Massachusetts and Rhode Island. A Coastal Plain species, occurring very locally from Massachusetts to Long Island, New York, southern New Jersey, and Delaware, North Carolina, South Carolina and Florida.

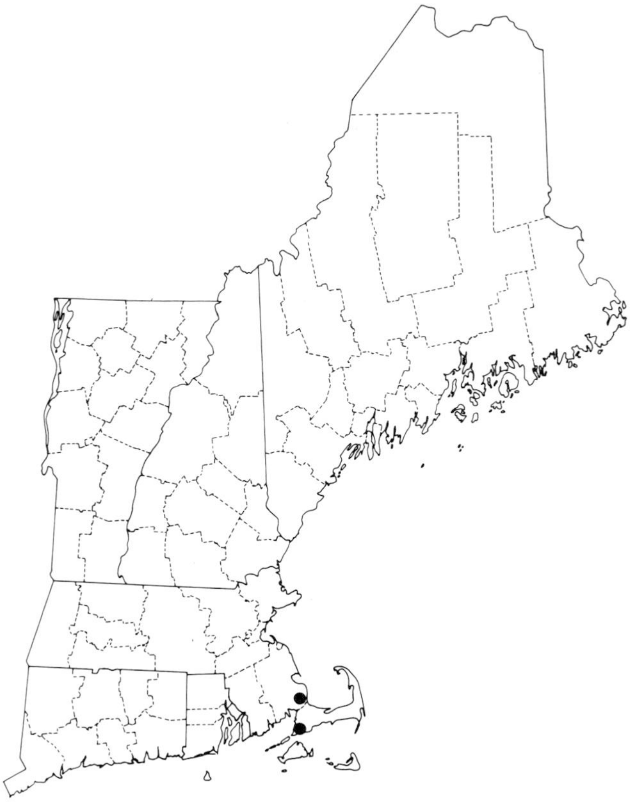

Map 43
Rhynchospora inundata

Fig. 38.   Horned-rush *(Rhynchospora inundata)*:   Habit X.8; achene showing long beak and bristles X5.

Scirpus hallii Gray (Hall's Bulrush). Map 44. A plant of peaty and sandy shores, historically known in New England from two sites in Massachusetts; the Winter Pond population (Winchester, Massachusetts) apparently extirpated. Occurs very locally from Georgia and Florida to Texas; South Dakota, Nebraska, Kansas, Oklahoma, Missouri, and Illinois (appears best established in the Great Plains region).

Map 44
Scirpus hallii

GRAMINEAE/POACEAE (Grass Family)

Calamagrostis inexpansa Gray var. *novae-angliae* Stebbins (New England Reedgrass). Map 45. A plant of moist cliffs and ledges and of low woods. Endemic to northern New England. In a recent revision of the genus *Calamagrostis* in eastern North America C. W. Greene now treats this taxon as a synonym within his concept of *Calamagrostis stricta* (Timm) Koeler subsp. *stricta* var. *inexpansa* (Gray) C. W. Greene, thus it has been dropped from further listing consideration by the U.S. Fish and Wildlife Service.

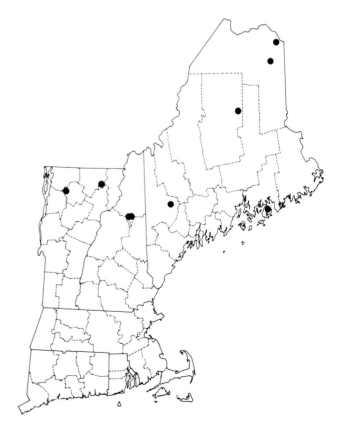

Map 45
Calamagrostis inexpansa var. *novae-angliae*

Calamagrostis lacustris (Kearney) Nash (Reedgrass). Map 46. Occurring on wet cliffs and ledges in New England. Also growing on shores, damp rocks, gravel or peaty sites from Labrador to northern Ontario, south locally to western Newfoundland; disjunct to the mountains of northern New England. C. W. Greene's revision treats this taxon as *C. stricta* (Timm) Koeler subsp. *inexpansa* (Gray) C. W. Greene var. *lacustris* (Kearney) C. W. Greene. New England specimens identified as *C. fernaldii*, annotated by Greene, fall within this taxon.

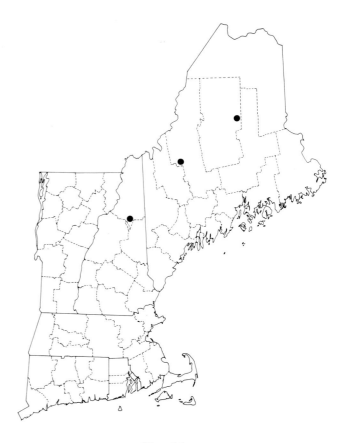

Map 46
Calamagrostis lacustris

Deschampsia atropurpurea (Wahlenb.) Sheele (Purple Hair-grass). Map 47. Alpine meadows, rocky slopes, and cool, wet ravines of Mt. Washington, New Hampshire, Mt. Katahdin and Mt. Bigelow, Maine; Mt. Mansfield (extinct?), Vermont. Widely distributed in boreal regions of North America, south in the mountains to Colorado; disjunct in the east to the mountains of northern New England; Eurasia.

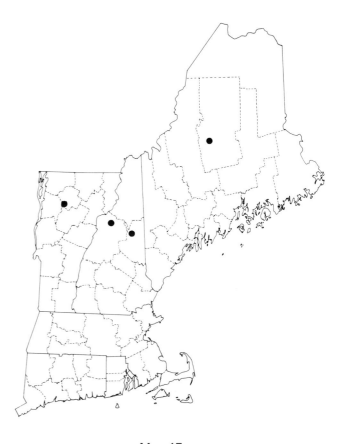

Map 47
Deschampsia atropurpurea

Festuca prolifera (Piper) Fern. (Proliferous Fescue). Fig. 39. Map 48. Wet slopes of alpine headwalls on Mt. Washington, New Hampshire and Mt. Katahdin, Maine. Restricted overall distribution, from the mountains of western Newfoundland and the Gaspé Peninsula, Quebec; disjunct to New England.

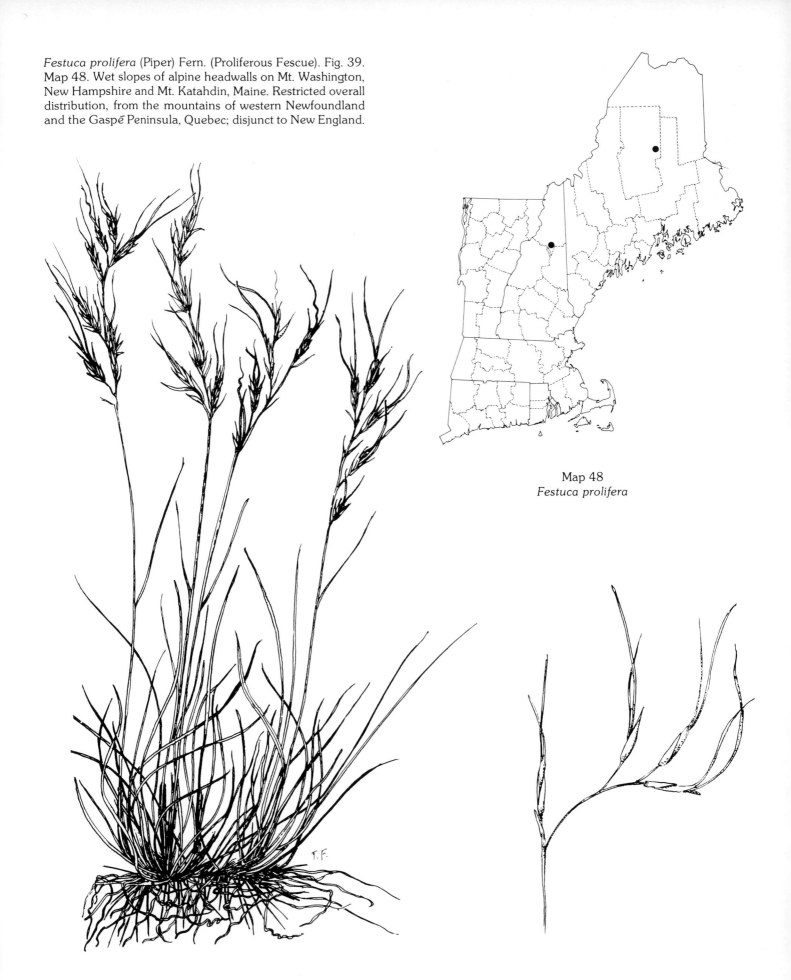

Map 48
Festuca prolifera

Fig. 39.   Proliferous Fescue *(Festuca prolifera)*:   Habit X.7; upper portion showing florets replaced by leafy tufts X2.

Poa alpigena (Fries) Lindm. f. (Alpine Bluegrass). Fig. 40.
Map 49. Alpine meadows of Mt. Washington, New Hampshire
and a single boggy site at Presque Isle, Maine. Widespread in
boreal North America; disjunct to northern New England;
Eurasia.

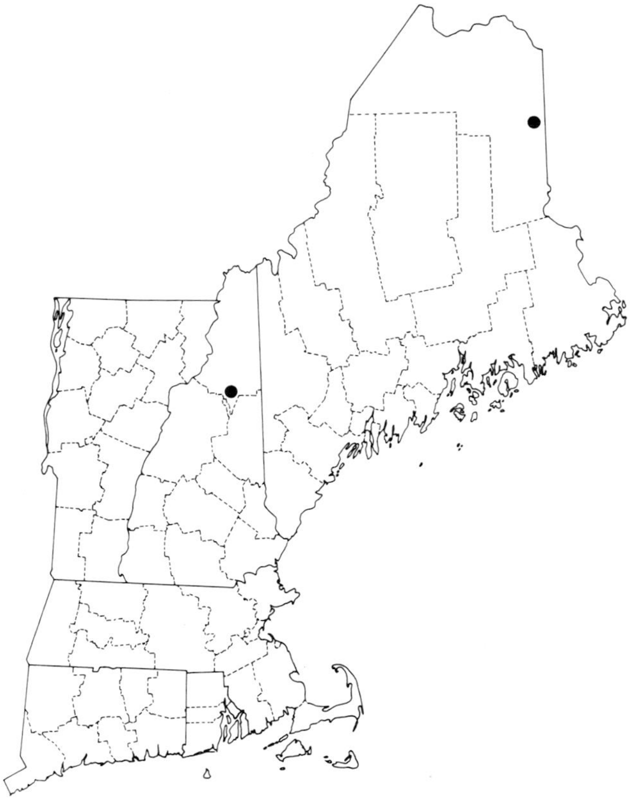

Map 49
Poa alpigena

Fig. 40.   Alpine Bluegrass *(Poa alpigena)*:   Habit X1; inflorescence X1; spikelet of florets X5; single floret showing cobwebby tuft of hairs at base X10.

Trisetum spicatum (L.) Ritcher var. *pilosiglume* Fern. (Spiked Trisetum). Fig. 41. Map 50. Moist alpine meadows and gravelly slides of Mt. Washington, New Hampshire, Mt. Mansfield, Vermont, and Mt. Katahdin, Maine. The taxon ranges from Labrador to western Lake Superior, south in the east to Cape Breton, Nova Scotia; disjunct to northern New England.

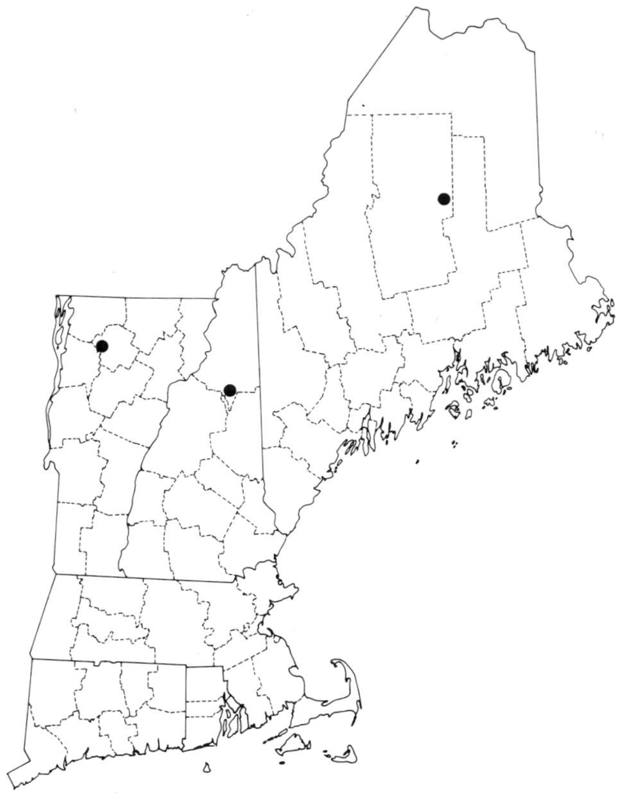

Map 50
Trisetum spicatum var. *pilosiglume*

Fig. 41.   Spiked Trisetum *(Trisetum spicatum* var. *pilosiglume)*:   Habit X.9; spikelet of florets X5.

JUNCACEAE (Rush Family)

Juncus stygius L. var. *americanus* Buchenau (American Stygx-rush). Fig. 42. Map 51. Boggy pools and sphagnum of calcareous areas; two sites in northern Maine. Boreal North America from southern Labrador to Saskatchewan, south to northern Maine, Michigan, and Minnesota.

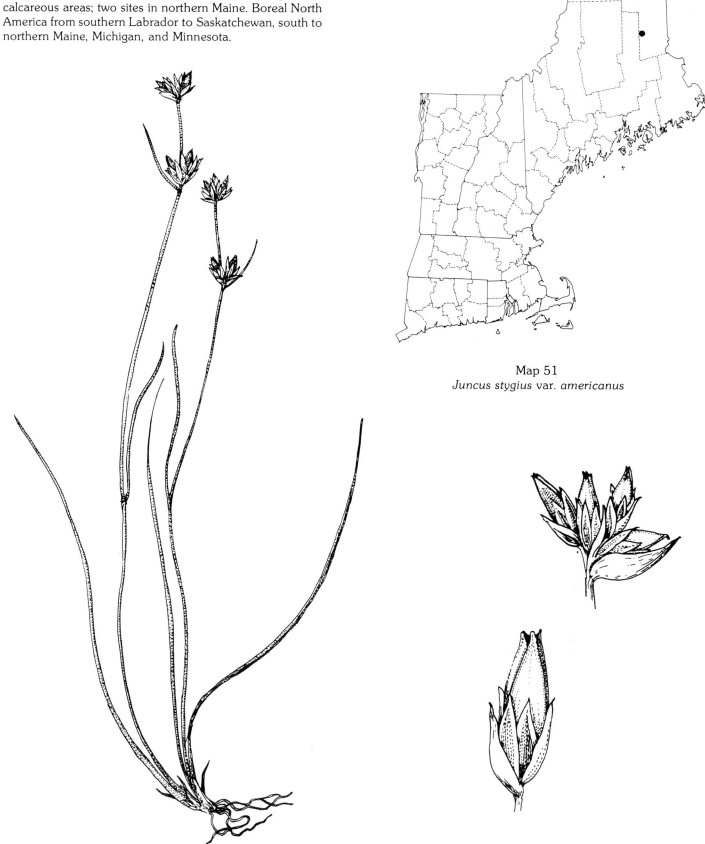

Map 51
Juncus stygius var. *americanus*

Fig. 42. American Stygx-rush *(Juncus stygius* var. *americanus)*: Habit X.9; cluster of fruits X3; single fruit X5.

75

Luzula confusa Lindeberg (Northern Woodrush). Fig. 43. Map 52. Cool, wet meadows and ravines of Mt. Washington, New Hampshire and Mt. Katahdin, Maine. Ranges from arctic regions south to alpine areas of the mountains of the Gaspé Peninsula, Quebec, Maine, and New Hampshire.

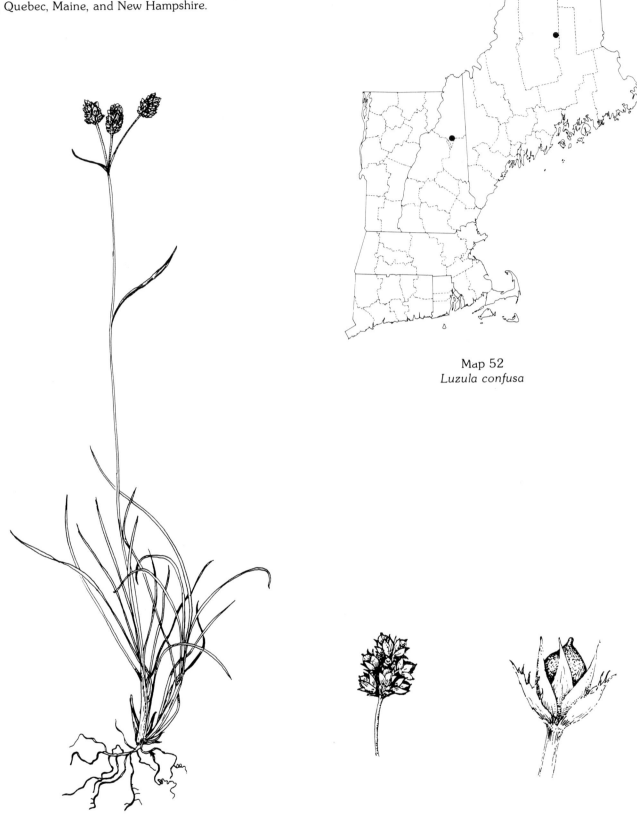

Map 52
Luzula confusa

Fig. 43. Northern Woodrush *(Luzula confusa):* Habit X.9; clusters of fruits X2; capsule with perianth parts subtended by bracts X10.

ORCHIDACEAE (Orchid Family)

Calypso bulbosa (L.) Oakes (Calypso). Fig. 44. Map 53.
Growing in mossy Northern White Cedar *(Thuja occidentalis)*
woods, chiefly calcareous areas. Declining in New England,
perhaps extinct in New Hampshire. Widely distributed in
boreal North America, but now very local.

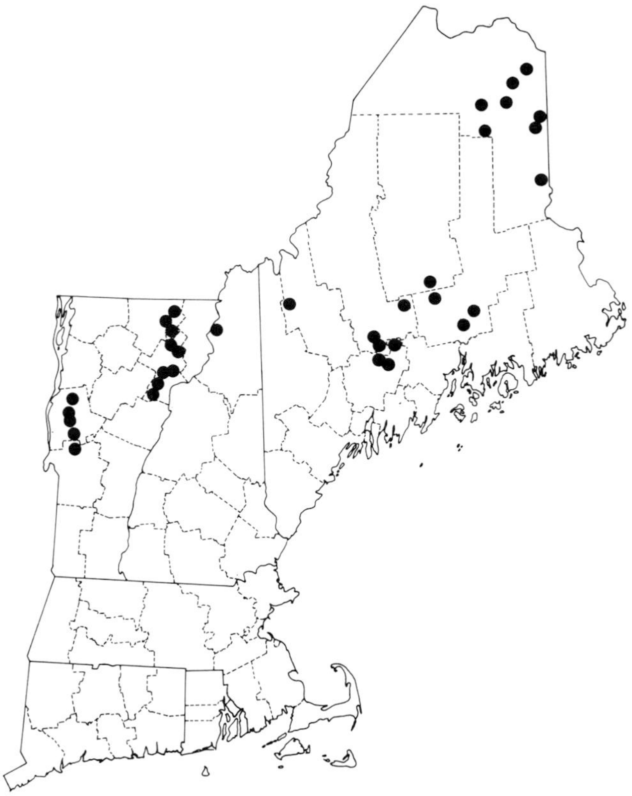

Map 53
Calypso bulbosa

Fig. 44. Calypso *(Calypso bulbosa):* Habit X.8; flower X3.

77

Cypripedium arietinum R. Br. (Ram's-head Lady's-slipper). Fig. 45. Map 54. Generally acid soils of swamps and bogs; also moist to dry, rich, wooded hillsides. Ranges from Quebec to Manitoba, south to New England, New York, Michigan, Wisconsin, Minnesota, Manitoba, and Saskatchewan; rare in the southern portion of its range. Declining; much rarer in New England than historical records suggest. The plant has not been seen in New Hampshire since 1939 (in spite of intensive field work by F. E. Brackley) and only a few Vermont stations have recently been documented. Only four of Maine's eleven sites have modern documentation. Connecticut's single site appears extirpated and the plant is possibly extinct in Massachusetts as well.

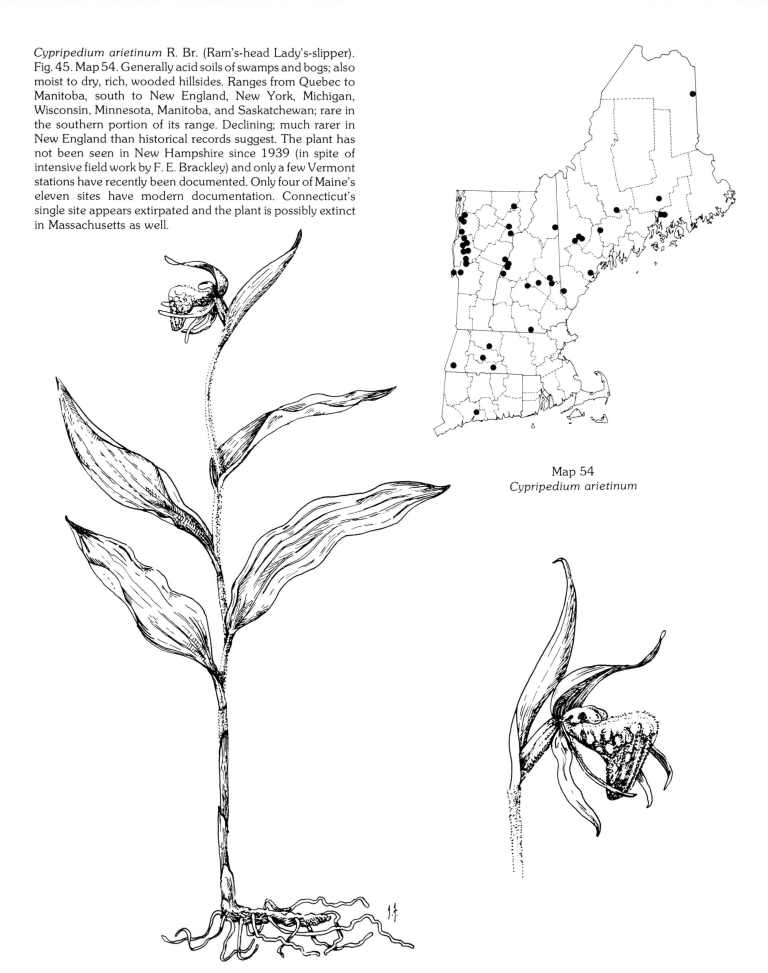

Map 54
Cypripedium arietinum

Fig 45.   Ram's-head Lady's-slipper *(Cypripedium arietinum)*:   Habit X.8; flower X2.

Listera australis Lindl. (Southern Twayblade). Fig. 46. Map 55. Known in New England only from two sphagnum bogs in Vermont. Ranges from Florida to Louisiana, north to southern Virginia and Tennessee; very locally to Vermont, southwestern Quebec, western New York, and southeastern Ontario.

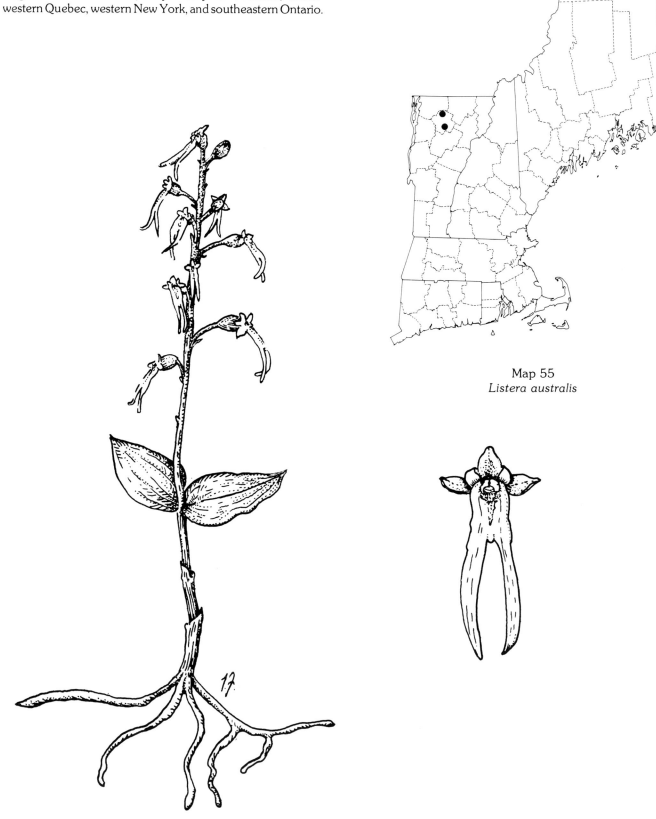

Map 55
Listera australis

Fig. 46.   Southern Twayblade *(Listera australis)*:   Habit X1; flower X4.

Orchis rotundifolia Banks ex Pursh (Small Round-leafed Orchis). Fig. 47. Map 56. Cool, wet Northern White Cedar *(Thuja occidentalis)* woods in Maine; three historical records from Vermont, but the plant is now believed extirpated in that state. Chiefly of low arctic regions of northwestern North America, rare and very local eastward. (Sometimes treated as *Amerorchis rotundifolia* (Banks ex Pursh) Hult.)

Map 56
Orchis rotundifolia

Fig. 47.   Small Round-leaved Orchis *(Orchis rotundifolia)*:   Habit X1; flower X3.

DICOTS

BETULACEAE (Birch Family)

Betula glandulosa Michx. (Dwarf Birch). Fig. 48. Map 57. Alpine slopes of Mt. Washington, New Hampshire and Mt. Katahdin, Maine; Colchester Bog (hybrid?), Vermont. Ranging widely in the low arctic of North America, southward along the western mountains; disjunct in the east to northern New England and the Adirondack Mountains, New York.

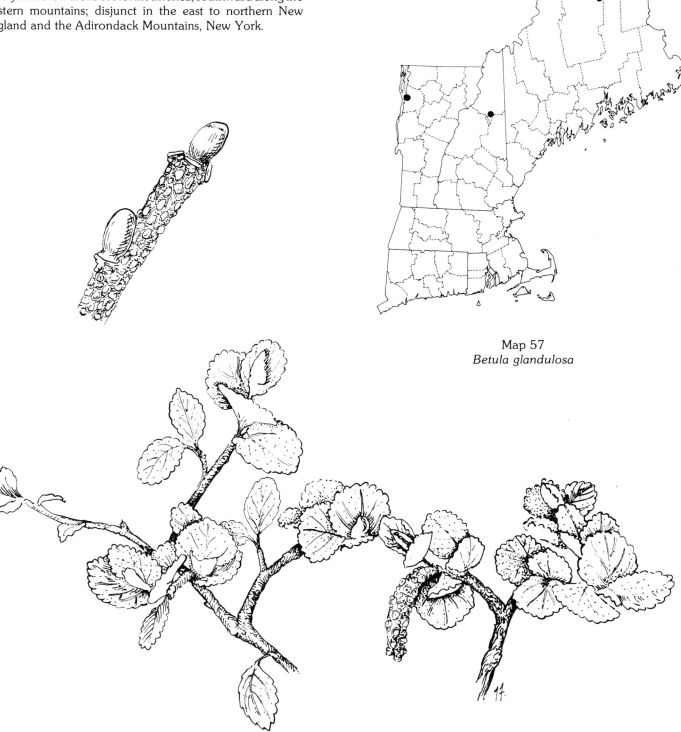

Map 57
Betula glandulosa

Fig. 48.   Dwarf Birch *(Betula glandulosa)*: Habit X1; segment of twig showing glands X5.

Betula minor (Tuckerm.) Fern. (Dwarf White Birch) Map 58. Alpine slopes of the Presidential and Franconia Ranges, New Hampshire, and Mt. Katahdin, Maine. Limited distribution, occupying rocky barrens, peats, and alpine summits from Labrador south to Newfoundland, Gaspé Peninsula and Laurentide Mountains, Quebec; disjunct to northern New England and the Adirondack Mountains, New York. Apparently of hybrid origin between *B. glandulosa* and *B. papyrifera*.

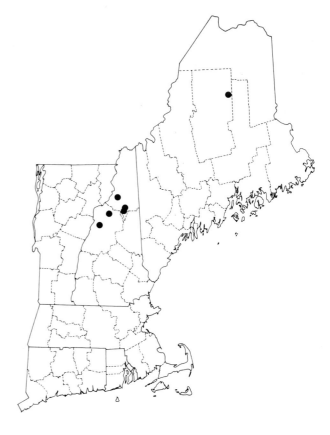

Map 58
Betula minor

CARYOPHYLLACEAE   (Pink or Sandwort Family)

Minuartia rubella (Wahlenb.) Hiern. (Arctic Sandwort). Fig. 49. Map 59. A single New England station on calcareous cliffs and ledges of Smuggler's Notch, Vermont. A wide ranging arctic-alpine species; circumpolar distribution. (synonym: *Arenaria rubella* Wahlenb.)

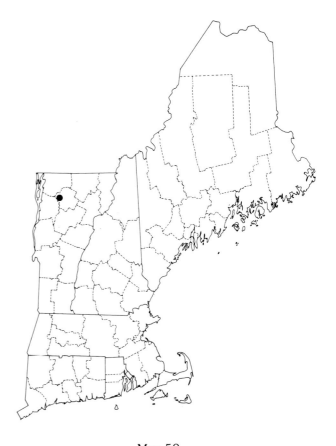

Map 59
Minuartia rubella

Fig. 49. Arctic Sandwort *(Minuartia rubella)*: Habit X1; flower X4.

COMPOSITAE/ASTERACEAE (Aster or Sunflower Family)

Achillea borealis Bong. (Northern Yarrow). Fig. 50. Map 60. Gravelly sites, ledges, roadsides, and gravelly beaches in northern New Hampshire and Maine. A boreal-arctic species ranging widely in northern North America, extending into eastern Asia.

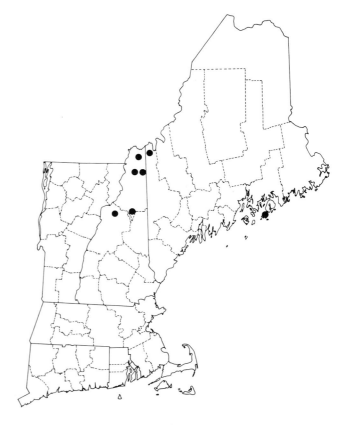

Map 60
Achillea borealis

Fig. 50. Northern Yarrow (*Achillea borealis*): Habit X.9; head of flowers X3.

Gnaphalium supinum L. (Alpine Cudweed). Fig. 51. Map 61. Grows in unstable gravels at the base of ravine headwalls of Mt. Washington, New Hampshire, and Mt. Katahdin, Maine. Arctic areas; amphi-Atlantic distribution.

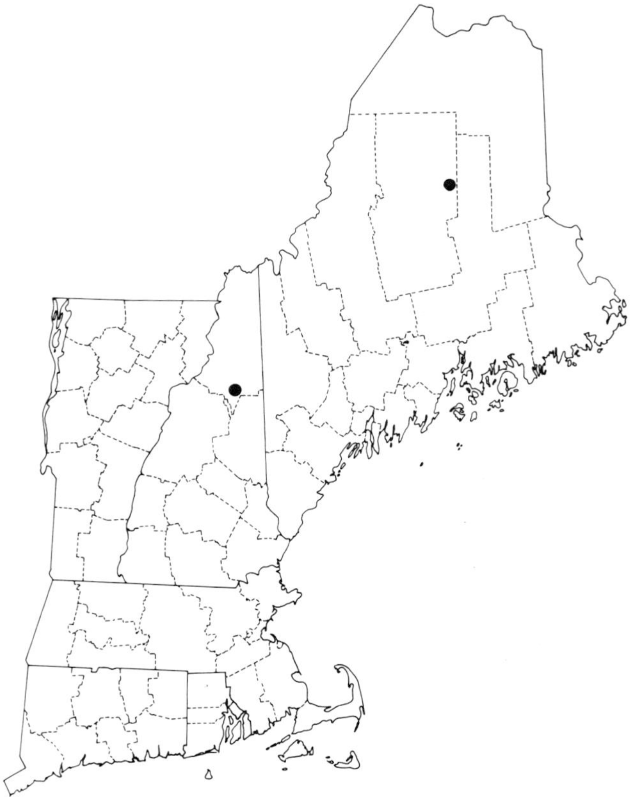

Map 61
Gnaphalium supinum

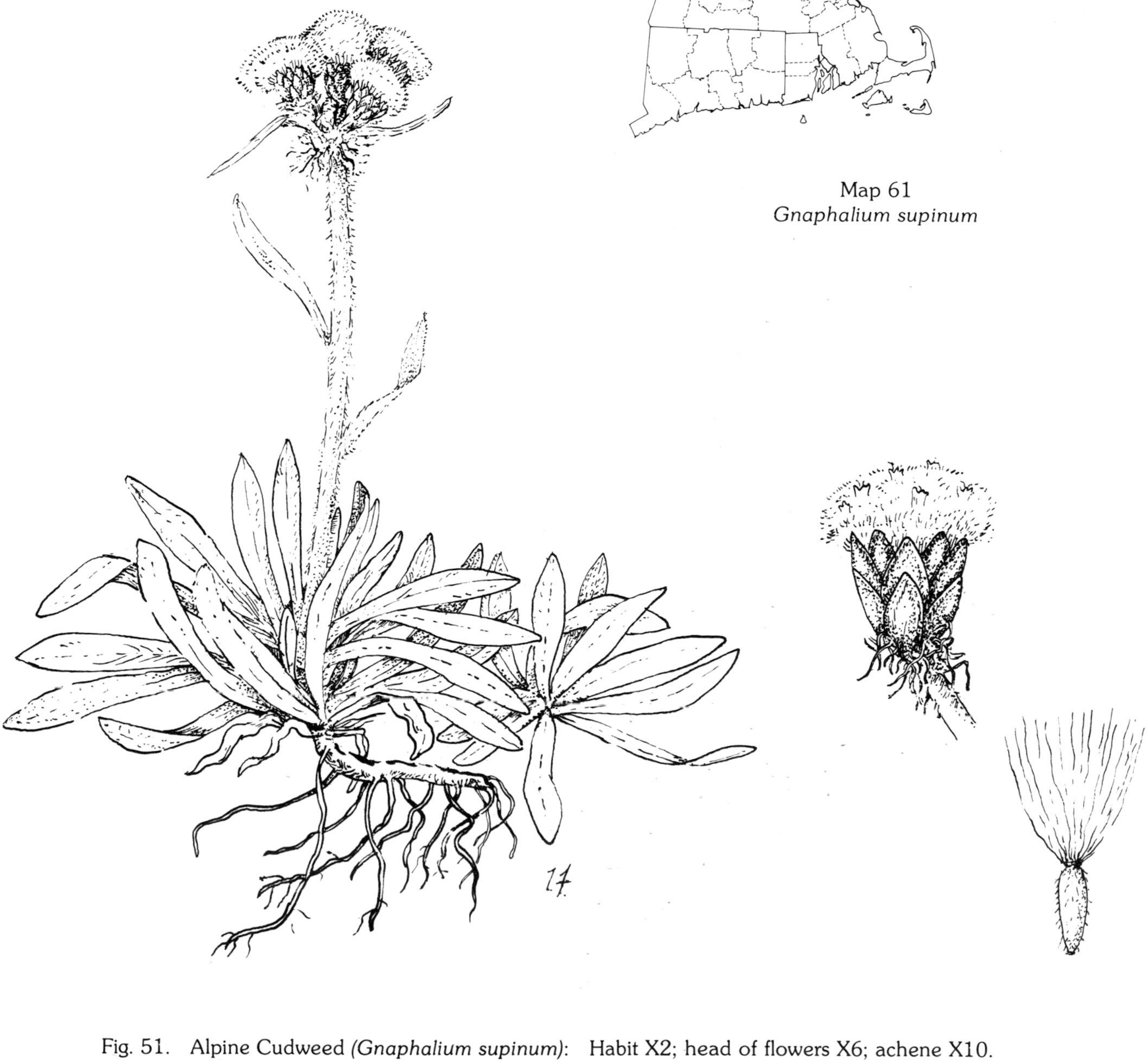

Fig. 51. Alpine Cudweed *(Gnaphalium supinum)*:   Habit X2; head of flowers X6; achene X10.

Solidago calcicola Fern. (Lime-loving Goldenrod). Fig. 52.
Map 62. A plant of rich woods and rocky or gravelly thickets in
northern New England. Restricted distribution from Newfoundland to northwestern Quebec and northern New England.

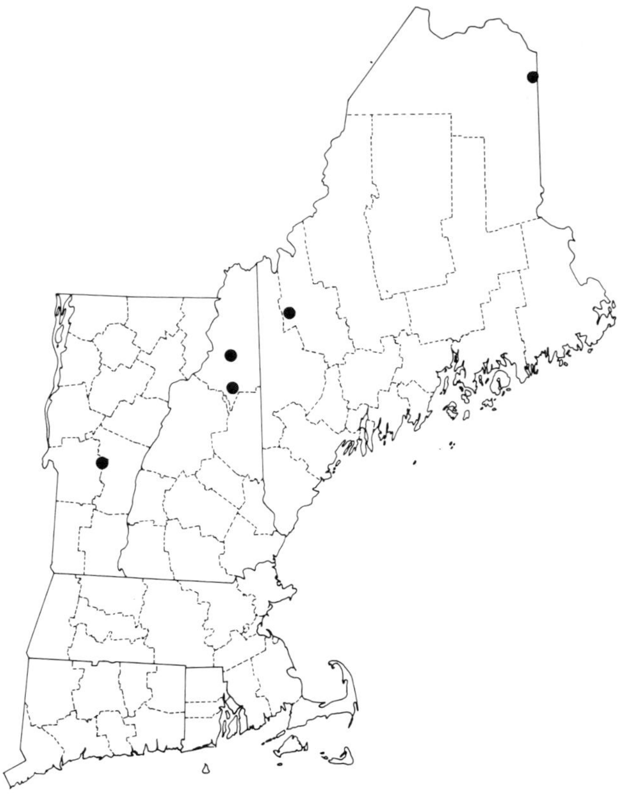

Map 62
Solidago calcicola

Fig. 52.   Lime-loving Goldenrod *(Solidago calcicola)*:   Habit X.8; head of flowers X3; achene X10.

Tanacetum huronense Nutt. var. *johannense* Fern. (St. John River Tansy). Fig. 53. Map 63. Endemic to gravels and sands of the St. John and Restigouche Rivers and tributaries, Quebec, New Brunswick, and Maine. Vigorous colonies occur along the St. John River.

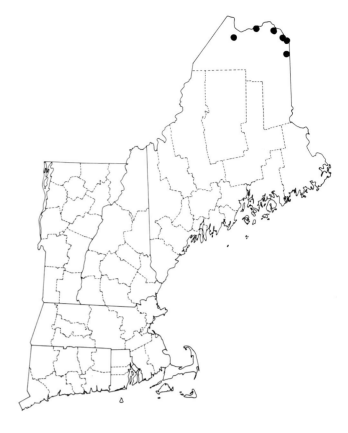

Map 63
Tanacetum huronense var. *johannense*

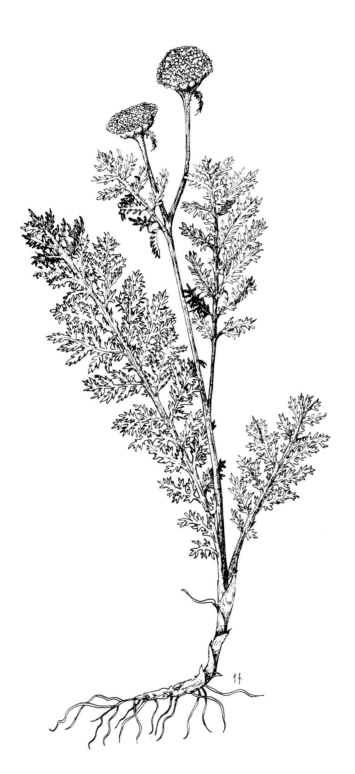

Fig. 53. St. John River Tansy (*Tanacetum huronense* var. *johannense*): Habit X.7.

CRUCIFERAE/BRASSICACEAE (Mustard Family)

Cardamine bellidifolia L. (Alpine Cress). Fig. 54. Map 64. Wet, mossy rocks and gravels bordering alpine brooks in cool ravines and shores of alpine ponds of Mt. Washington, New Hampshire and Mt. Katahdin, Maine, and along a mountain stream in West Baldwin, Maine. An arctic-alpine species; circumpolar distribution.

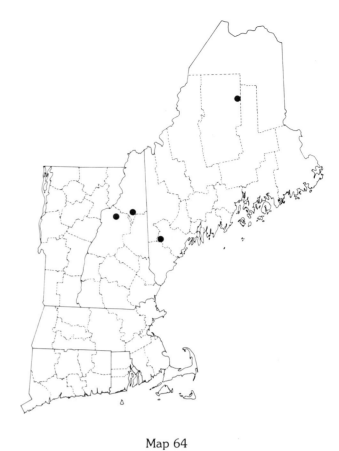

Map 64
Cardamine bellidifolia

Fig. 54. Alpine Cress *(Cardamine bellidifolia)*: Habit X2.

Draba glabella Pursh var. *glabella* (Smooth Draba). Map 65.
Known from a literature report for Willoughby, Vermont, but
documenting specimens have not been located for verifica-
tion. Ranges from Arctic regions south chiefly on calcareous
rock to Newfoundland, Quebec, Lake Champlain, New York,
and Hudson Bay ; Eurasia.

Map 65
Draba glabella var. *glabella*

Draba glabella Pursh var. *orthocarpa* Fern. (Smooth Draba).
Map 66. Limestone cliffs in Vermont; Salisbury locality a
literature report. Restricted range, Mingan Islands and Gaspé
Peninsula to Temiscouata, Quebec; Keewatin; disjunct to
Vermont.

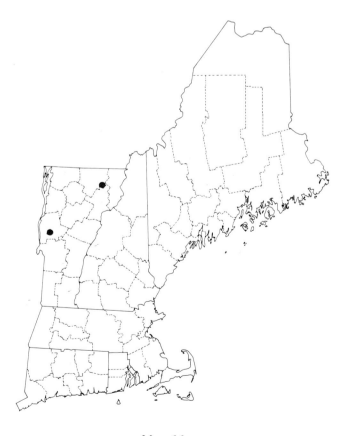

Map 66
Draba glabella var. *orthocarpa*

Draba lanceolata Royle (Lance-leaved Draba). Fig. 55. Map 67. Dry cliffs, ledges, and talus in northern New England. Widely distributed in western North America, rare eastward; Asia.

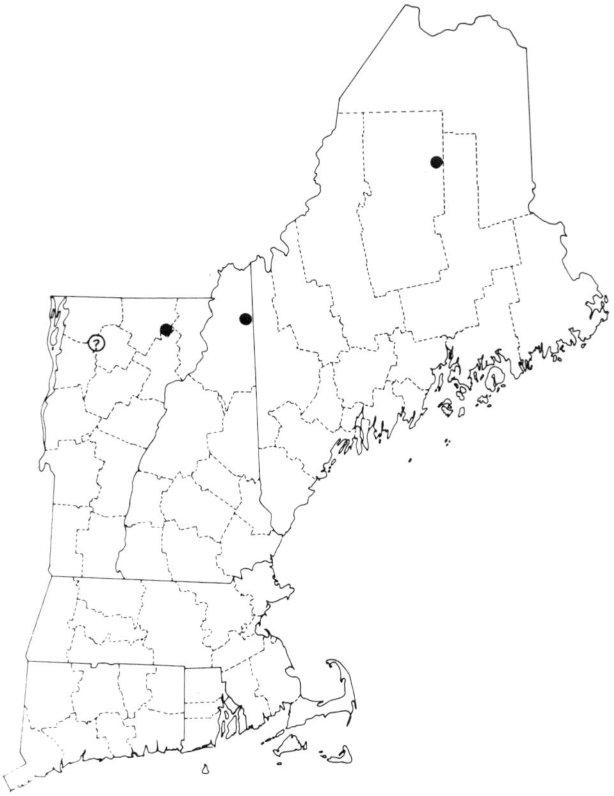

Map 67
Draba lanceolata

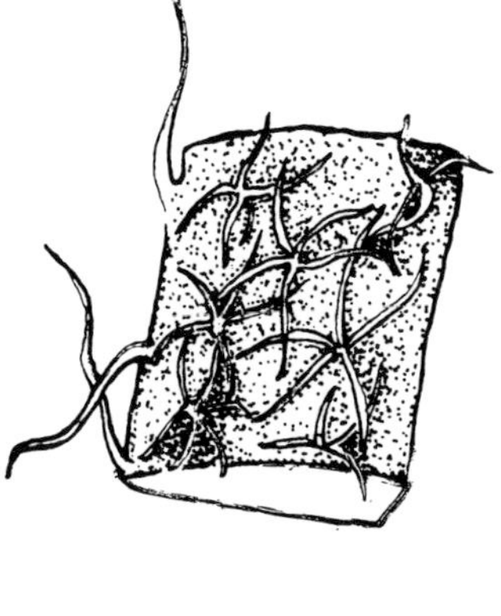

Fig. 55. Lance-leaved Draba *(Draba lanceolata)*: Habit X1; fruit X4; segment of leaf showing stellate hairs X20.

DIAPENSIACEAE (Diapensia Family)

Diapensia lapponica L. subsp. *lapponica* (Diapensia). Map 68. Exposed alpine ridges and summits blown free of snow on higher mountains of northern New England. Arctic regions, disjunct to New England; amphi-Atlantic distribution.

DROSERACEAE (Sundew Family)

Drosera anglica Huds. (Anglican Sundew). Fig. 56 Map 69. A single station newly discovered for New England by L. M. Eastman and C. Straus in calcareous portion of Crystal Bog, Crystal, Maine. Circumboreal distribution.

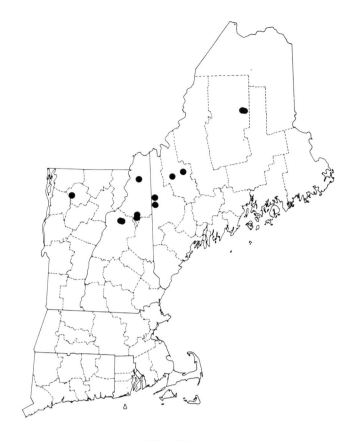

Map 68
Diapensia lapponica subsp. *lapponica*

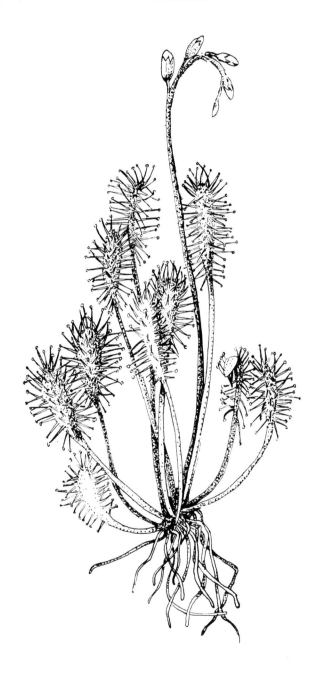

Fig. 56.   Anglican Sundew *(Drosera anglica)*:   Habit X2.

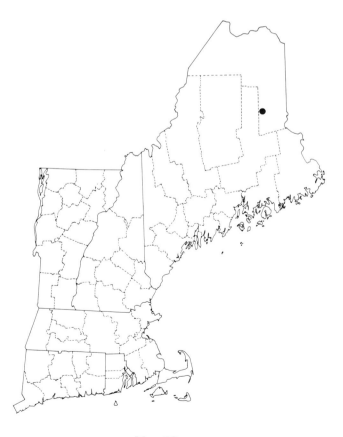

Map 69
Drosera anglica

Drosera linearis Goldie (Linear-leaved Sundew). Fig. 57. Map 70. A single station, calcareous portion of Crystal Bog, Crystal, Maine. Distributed in boreal regions of northeastern North America, south to northern Maine, Michigan, and Wisconsin.

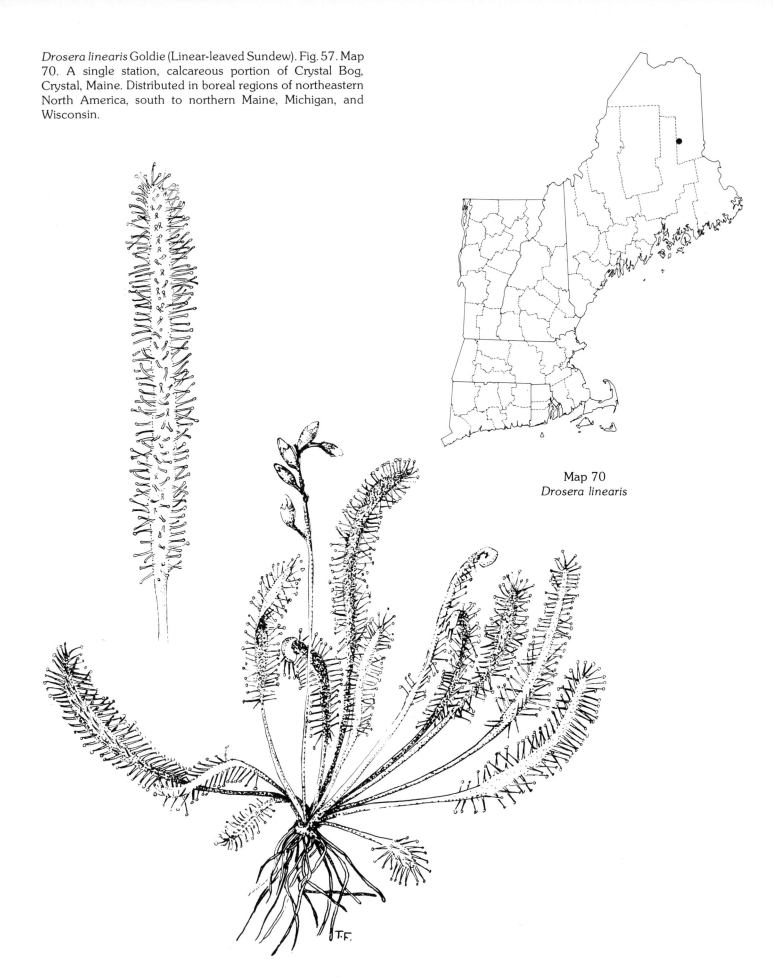

Map 70
Drosera linearis

Fig. 57.   Linear-leaved Sundew *(Drosera linearis)*: Habit X2; leaf with sticky glands X10.

ERICACEAE (Heath Family)

Arctostaphylos alpina (L.) Spreng. (Alpine Bearberry). Fig. 58
Map 71. Sparse in alpine meadows of the Presidential Range,
New Hampshire and Mt. Katahdin, Maine. Arctic regions,
disjunct to New England; circumpolar distribution.

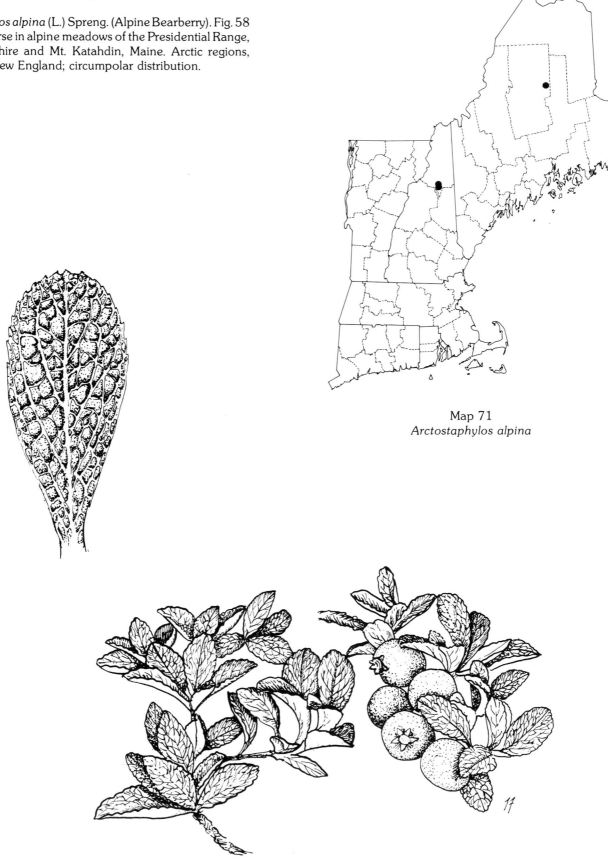

Map 71
Arctostaphylos alpina

Fig. 58.   Alpine Bearberry *(Arctostaphylos alpina)*   Habit X2; leaf showing vein pattern and texture X5.

Cassiope hypnoides (L.) D. Don (Moss Plant). Fig. 59. Map 72. Wet ledges and moist ravine headwalls of alpine sites of the Presidential Range, New Hampshire and Mt. Katahdin, Maine. Arctic regions, disjunct to New England; amphi-Atlantic distribution.

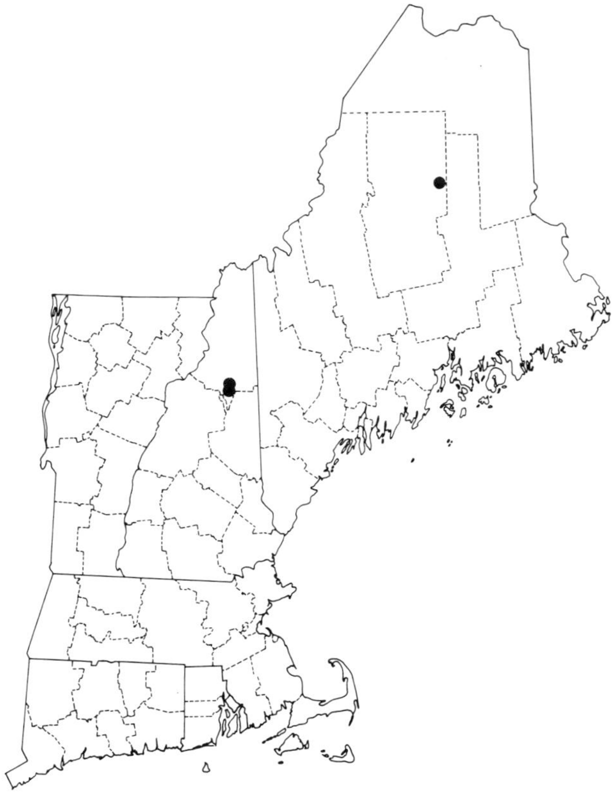

Map 72
Cassiope hypnoides

Fig. 59.   Moss Plant *(Cassiope hypnoides)*: Habit X3; previous year's persistent fruit X8.

Loiseleuria procumbens (L.) Desv. (Alpine Azalea). Map 73. Rocky or peaty exposed areas in the alpine zone of the Presidential and Franconia Ranges, New Hampshire and Mt. Katahdin, Maine. Arctic-alpine regions; circumpolar distribution (with gap in north central Siberia); disjunct in alpine areas in eastern North America to northern New England.

Phyllodoce caerulea (L.) Bab. (Mountain Heather or Heath). Fig. 60. Map 74. Rocky and peaty alpine slopes of the Presidential Range and Mt. Lafayette, New Hampshire and Mt. Katahdin, Maine. Arctic-alpine regions; circumpolar distribution (with some gaps); disjunction in alpine areas in eastern North America to northern New England.

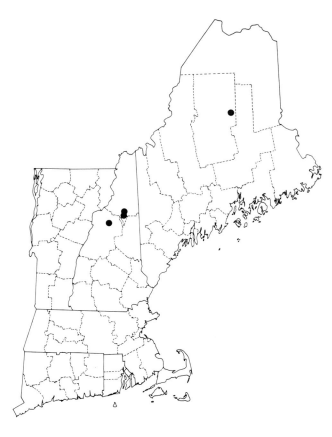

Map 73
Loiseleuria procumbens

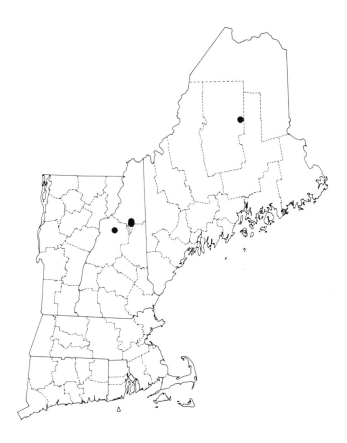

Map 74
Phyllodoce caerulea

Fig. 60.   Mountain Heather *(Phyllodoce caerulea)*: Habit X1; flowers X4.

Rhododendron lapponicum (L.) Wahlenb. (Lapland Rosebay). Map 75. Rocky and peaty alpine sites in the Presidential Range and Mt. Katahdin, Maine. Ranges widely in arctic regions of North America and western Asia; Greenland and Scandinavia; disjunct in eastern North America to the Wisconsin Dells and alpine areas to northern New England.

Vaccinium boreale Hall and Aalders (Alpine Blueberry). Fig. 61. Map 76. Alpine meadows and ridges of higher mountains of Maine, New Hampshire, and Vermont. Ranges from northeastern Quebec and Labrador to Newfoundland, Cape Breton, Nova Scotia, and the Gaspé Peninsula, Quebec; disjunct to alpine summits of northern New England and the Adirondack Mountains, New York. This species was only recently described (1966) and many specimens of high elevations identified as *V. angustifolium* may actually be *V. boreale*.

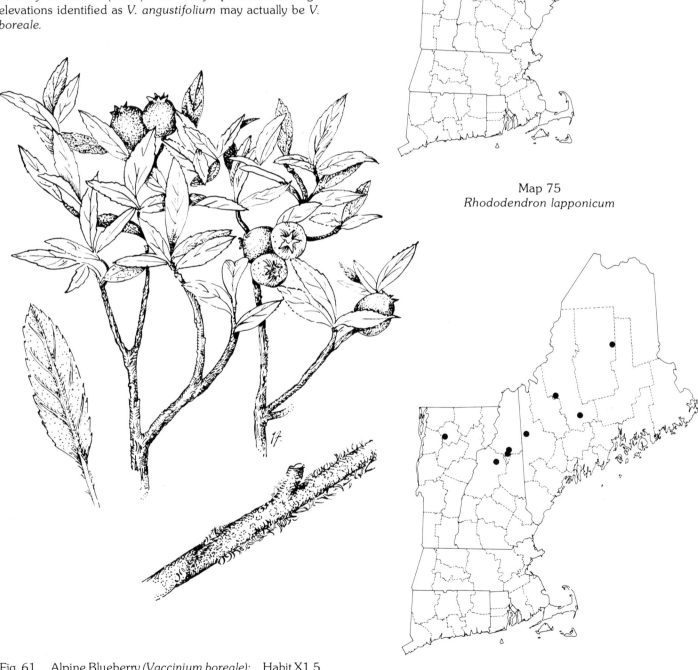

Map 75
Rhododendron lapponicum

Map 76
Vaccinium boreale

Fig. 61. Alpine Blueberry *(Vaccinium boreale):*   Habit X1.5 segment of stem with pubescence in lines X5; leaf with serrate margin X3.

GENTIANACEAE (Gentian Family)

Sabatia kennedyana Fern. (Plymouth Gentian or Large Sabatia). Fig. 62. Map 77. Sandy, peaty margins of shallow, Coastal Plain ponds of southeastern Massachusetts and Rhode Island. A disjunct Coastal Plain species of northeastern South Carolina and southeastern North Carolina, southwestern New England, and one population in Yarmouth County, Nova Scotia.

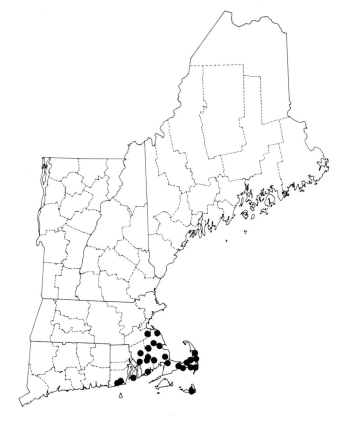

Map 77
Sabatia kennedyana

LEGUMINOSAE/FABACEAE (Pea or Bean Family)

Hedysarum alpinum L. var. *americanum* Michx. (Alpine Hedysarum). Fig. 63. Map 78. Limestone cliffs and ledges in Vermont and rocky, gravelly shores and riverbanks in calcareous areas of northern Maine. In boreal regions, chiefly growing on calcareous rocks and gravels from Newfoundland to Alaska, south to northern New England, north shore of Lake Superior, Saskatchewan, and Alberta; disjunct on the eastern side of the Cordillera in Wyoming.

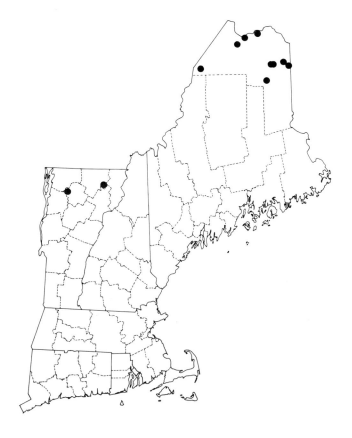

Map 78
Hedysarum alpinum var. *americanum*

Fig. 62.   Plymouth Gentian *(Sabatia kennedyana)*: Habit X1; young fruit X8.

Fig. 63. Alpine Hedysarum *(Hedysarum alpinum* var. *americanum)*: Habit X1; flower X5; fruit X5.

NYMPHAEACEAE (Water-lily Family)

Nymphaea tetragona Georgi subsp. *leibergii* (Morong) Porsild (Small White Water-lily). Fig. 64. Map 79. Hardwater ponds and quiet streams in northern Maine. Very rare throughout its range, from northern Maine and Quebec to British Columbia and Alaska. Porsild states that this is one of Canada's rarest plants. Known in the United States only from northern regions of Maine, Michigan (Isle Royale), and Idaho.

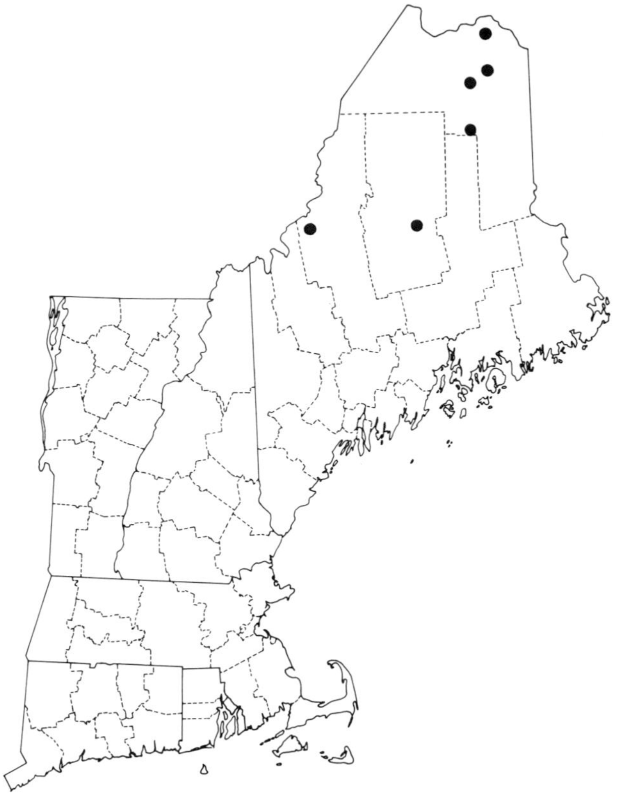

Map 79
Nymphaea tetragona subsp. *leibergii*

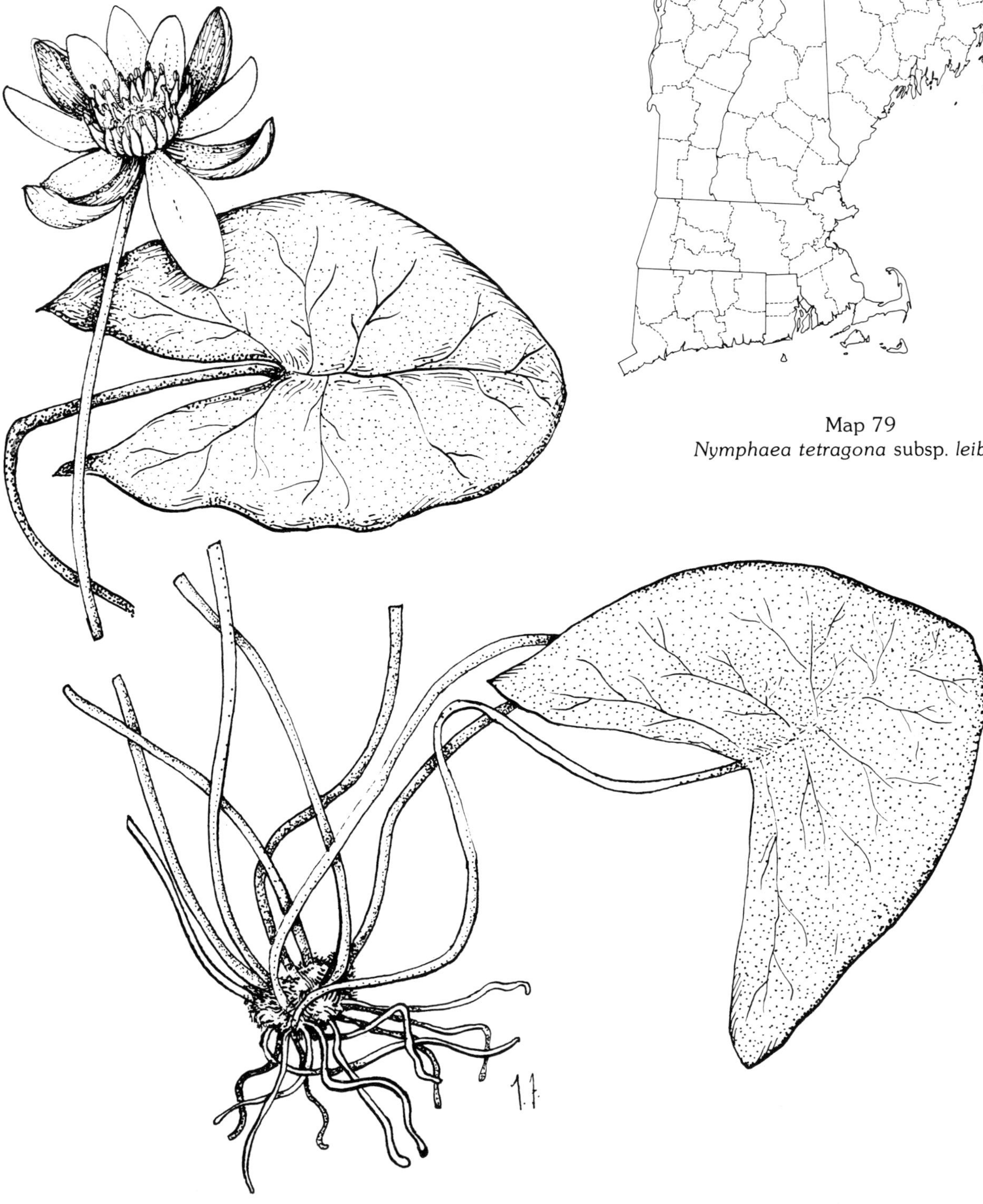

Fig. 64.   Small White Water-lily *(Nymphaea tetragona* subsp. *leibergii)*:   Habit showing floating leaf (above) and submersed leaf X1.

POLYGONACEAE (Buckwheat Family)

Polygonum viviparum L. var. *viviparum* (Alpine Bistort). Fig. 65. Map 80. Moist alpine meadows on Mt. Mansfield and Camel's Hump, Vermont, Mt. Washington, New Hampshire, and Mt. Katahdin, Maine. Circumpolar distribution. It has not been collected this century in Vermont.

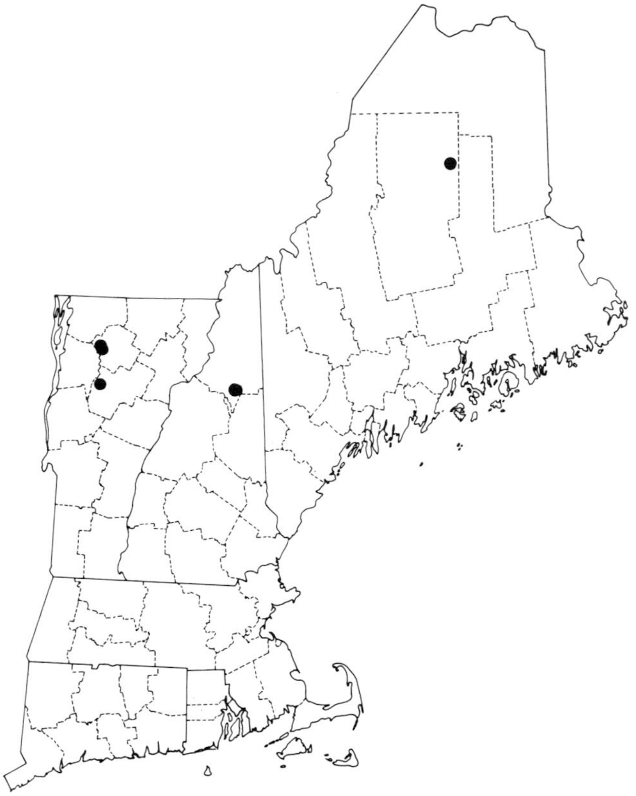

Map 80
Polygonum viviparum var. *viviparum*

Fig. 65.   Alpine Bistort *(Polygonum viviparum* var. *viviparum)*:   Habit X1; inflorescence showing flowers in upper portion and bulbils in lower portion X5.

RANUNCULACEAE

Hydrastis canadensis L. (Golden Seal). Fig. 66. Map 81. Rich woods, chiefly western New England. Widely ranging in eastern United States from Vermont to Minnesota, south to Georgia, Alabama, and Arkansas.

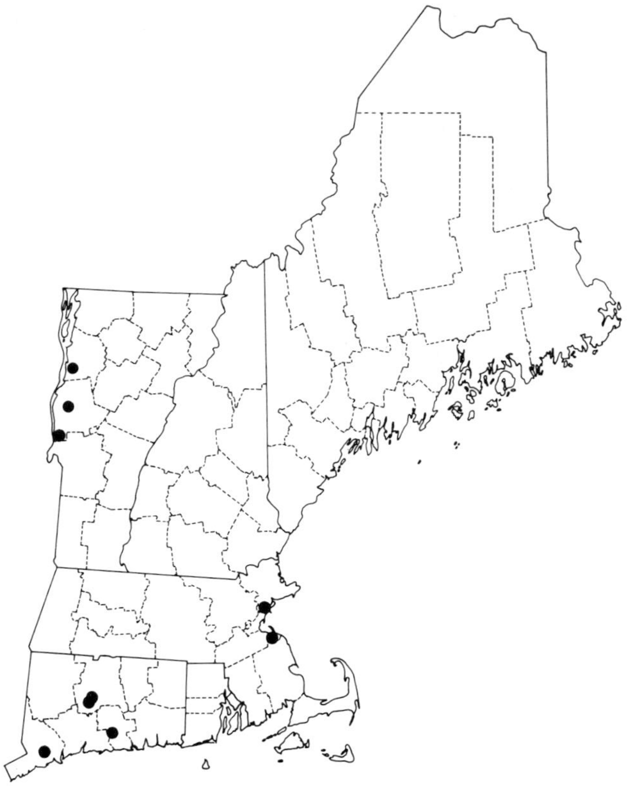

Map 81
Hydrastis canadensis

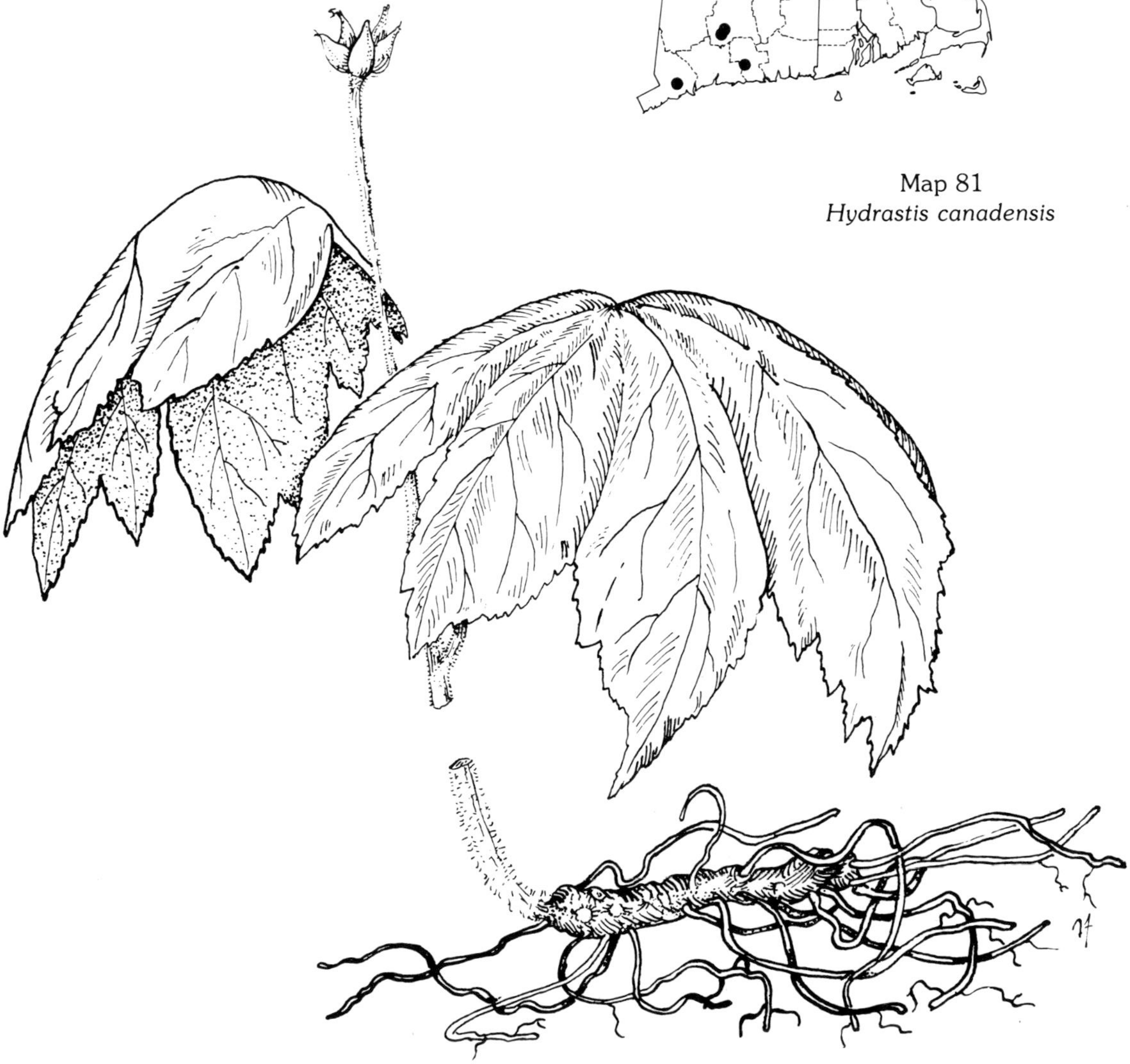

Fig. 66.   Golden Seal *(Hydrastis canadensis)*: Habit X1; rootstock X1.

Ranunculus lapponicus L. (Lapland Buttercup). Fig. 67. Map 82. Known in New England only from wet or boggy woods of northern Maine. Subarctic regions, circumpolar distribution.

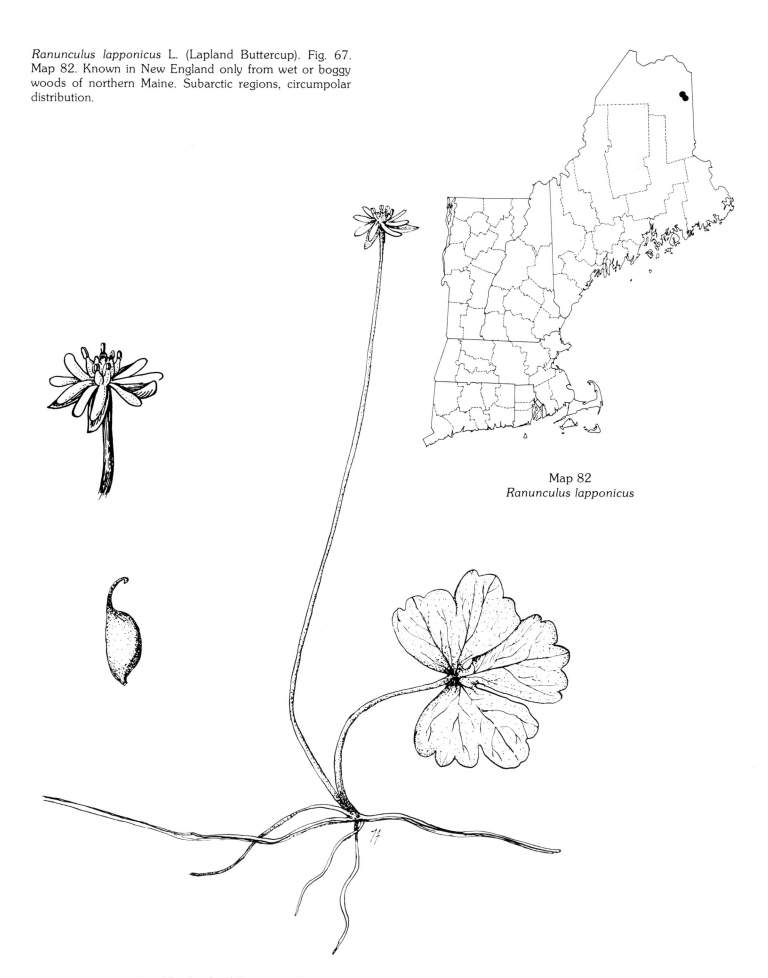

Map 82
Ranunculus lapponicus

Fig. 67. Lapland Buttercup *(Ranunculus lapponicus)*:   Habit X1; flower X2; achene X5.

ROSACEAE   (Rose Family)

Amelanchier nantucketensis Bickn. (Nantucket Juneberry). Fig. 68. Map 83. Endemic to moorlands of Nantucket and Martha's Vineyard Islands, Massachusetts. Well established, forming extensive thickets at some sites.

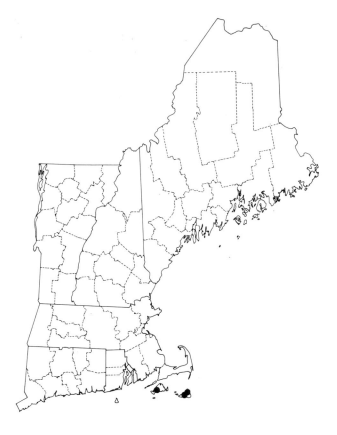

Map 83
Amelanchier nantucketensis

Fig. 68.   Nantucket Juneberry *(Amelanchier nantucketensis)*:   Habit X1; flower X3; fruiting branch X1.

Geum peckii Pursh (Mountain Avens). Map 84. Occurs in moist alpine meadows and cold, wet subalpine ravines; occasionally on wet rocks along mountain streams at slightly lower elevations. Endemic; known only from high elevations of the White Mountains, New Hampshire and one site, a raised coastal bog, on Brier Island, Digby, Cumberland County, Nova Scotia. Pictou County, Nova Scotia is also cited in the Flora of Canada, but specimens documenting a population for that locality have not been found.

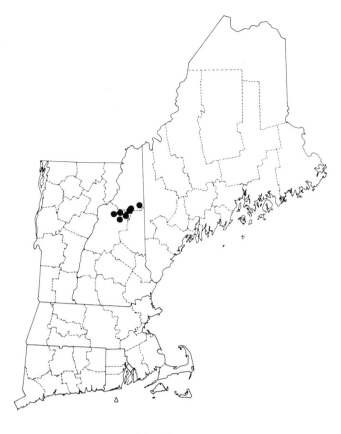

Map 84
Geum peckii

Prunus alleghaniensis Porter (Alleghany Plum). Map 85. Thickets along riverbanks and low ground at margins of woods in Connecticut. A rare and local species of dry, rocky woods from Connecticut to central Pennsylvania, along the mountains to western Virginia.

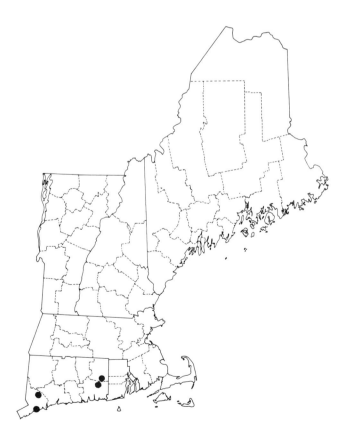

Map 85
Prunus alleghaniensis

105

RUBIACEAE (Madder Family)

Houstonia caerulea (L.) Hook. var. *faxonorum* Pease and Moore (Alpine Bluet). Map 86. Grows along moist stream borders and meadows in subalpine and alpine areas in New Hampshire. Endemic; one outlying station reported from St. Pierre et Miquelon Islands off the southern coast of Newfoundland. A critical examination of the taxonomic status of the variety is needed.

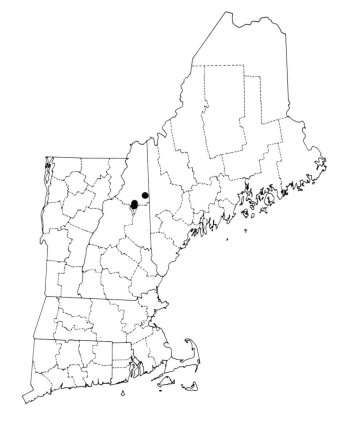

Map 86
Houstonia caerulea var. *faxonorum*

SALICACEAE (Willow Family)

Salix arctophila Cockerell ex Heller (Arctic Willow). Map 87. Known in New England only from a ravine headwall on Mt. Katahdin, Maine. Arctic regions from Greenland to northeastern Alaska, south in alpine sites to Newfoundland and the Gaspé Peninsula; disjunct to Maine.

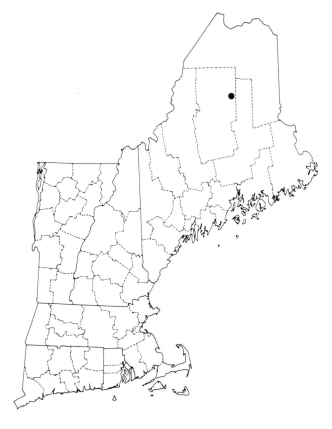

Map 87
Salix arctophila

Salix argyrocarpa Anderss. (Silver Willow). Fig. 69. Map 88. Moist alpine and subalpine meadows and ravines on Mt. Washington, New Hampshire and Mt. Katahdin, Maine.

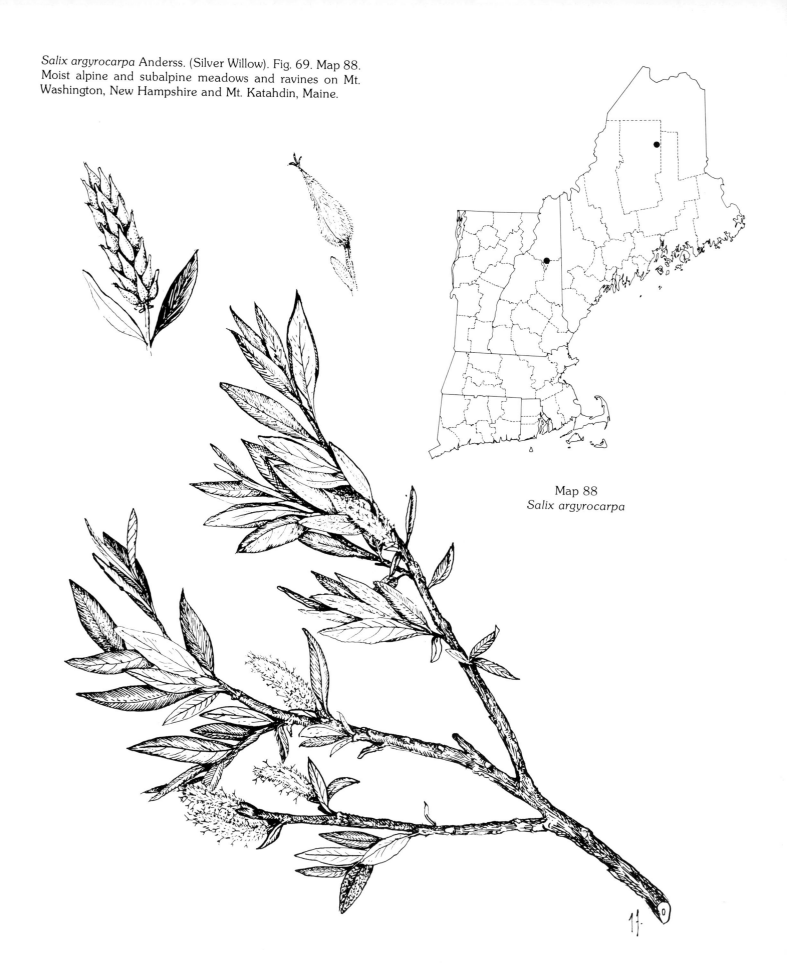

Map 88
Salix argyrocarpa

Fig. 69.   Silver Willow *(Salix argyrocarpa)*:   Habit X1; fruits X2; single fruit subtended by bract X5.

Salix herbacea L. (Dwarf Willow). Fig. 70. Map 89. Cold, wet alpine ravines, particularly in areas with late-lying snow, Franconia and Presidential Ranges, New Hampshire and Mt. Katahdin, Maine. Arctic-alpine regions, amphi-Atlantic distribution; disjunct to northern New England and the Adirondack Mountains, New York.

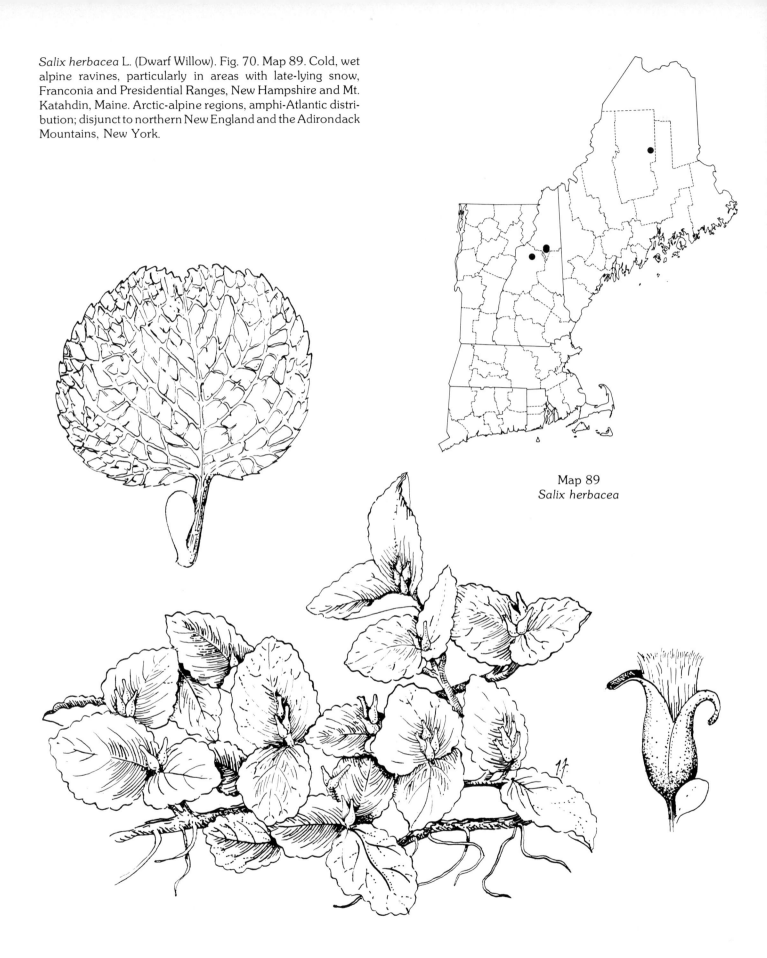

Map 89
Salix herbacea

Fig. 70.   Dwarf Willow *(Salix herbacea):*   Habit X2; single leaf X5; dehisced capsule X10.

Salix interior Rowlee var. *exterior* Fern. (Inside-outside Sandbar Willow). Map 90. Known only from sandbars and beaches of the Aroostook River, northern Maine and the Susquehanna River, southeastern Pennsylvania. The taxonomic status is somewhat doubtful.

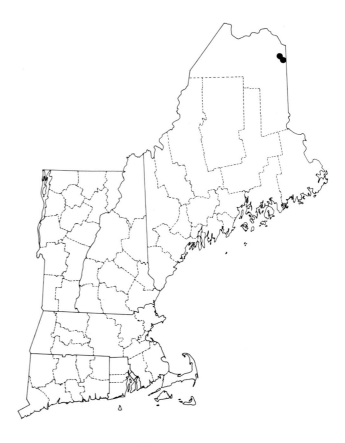

Map 90
Salix interior var. *exterior*

Salix X *peasei* Fern. (Pease's Willow). Map 91. Known only from mossy banks in King's Ravine, Mt. Adams (Presidential Range), New Hampshire and from Hudson Bay.

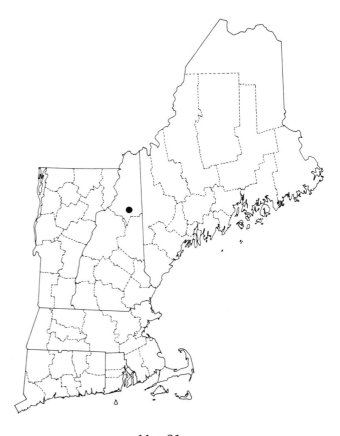

Map 91
Salix X *peasei*

SAXIFRAGACEAE (Saxifrage Family)

Saxifraga aizoides L. (Yellow Mountain Saxifrage). Fig. 71. Map 92. Occurring in New England on limestone cliffs and ledges in northern Vermont. Arctic regions, south on calcareous gravels to Newfoundland and eastern Quebec; disjunct to Vermont and western New York; amphi-Atlantic distribution.

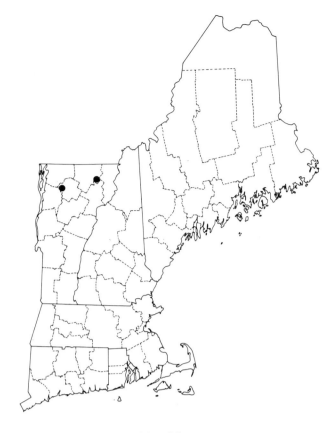

Map 92
Saxifraga aizoides

Fig. 71.   Yellow Mountain Saxifrage *(Saxifraga aizoides)*:   Habit X1; flower X4.

Saxifraga aizoon Jacq. var. *neogaea* Butters (Livelong Saxifrage). Fig. 72. Map 93. Calcareous rocks, ledges, and cliffs in Vermont, New Hampshire, and Maine. Calcareous sites in arctic regions of Northeastern North America and Greenland; disjunct in alpine sites to northern New England.

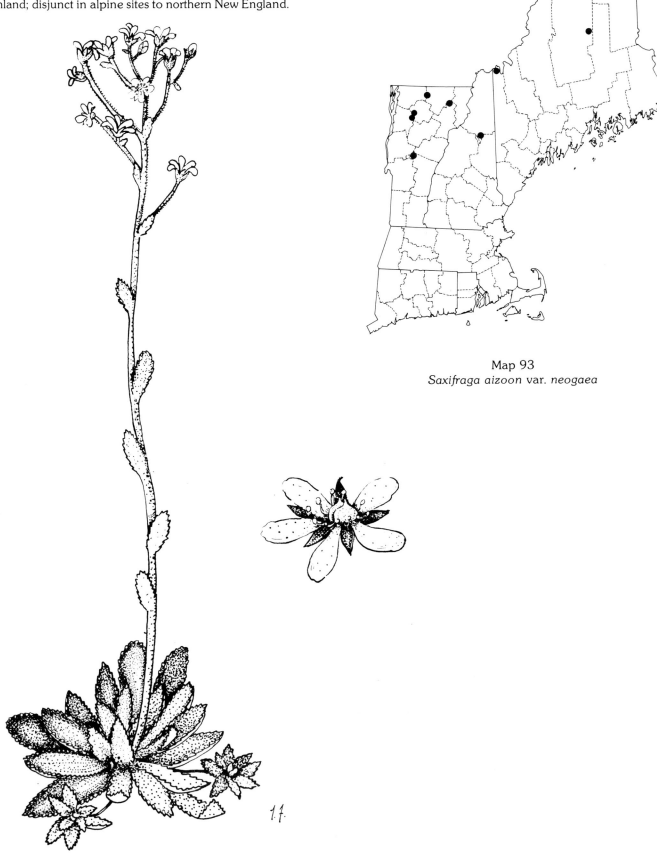

Map 93
Saxifraga aizoon var. *neogaea*

Fig. 72. Livelong Saxifrage *(Saxifraga aizoon* var. *neogaea)*: Habit X1; flower X4.

Saxifraga cernua L. (Nodding Saxifrage). Map 94. Known in New England only from the headwall of Huntington's Ravine, Mt. Washington, New Hampshire. Arctic regions, circumpolar distribution; disjunct to the Gaspé Peninsula, Quebec and New Hampshire.

Map 94
Saxifraga cernua

Saxifraga oppositifolia L. (Purple Mountain Saxifrage). Fig. 73. Map 95. Only known in New England from calcareous cliffs and ledges of Mt. Mansfield, Willoughby Cliffs, and Job Pond Cliffs, Vermont. A high arctic species, circumpolar distribution; disjunct to southern Labrador and western Newfoundland, the Gaspé Peninsula, Quebec, and Vermont.

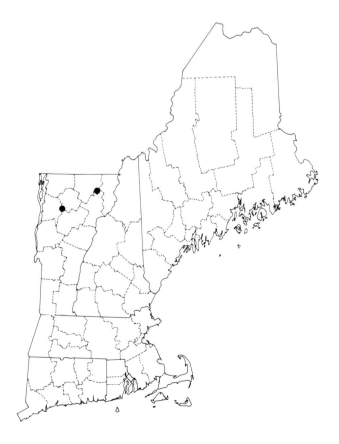

Map 95
Saxifraga oppositifolia

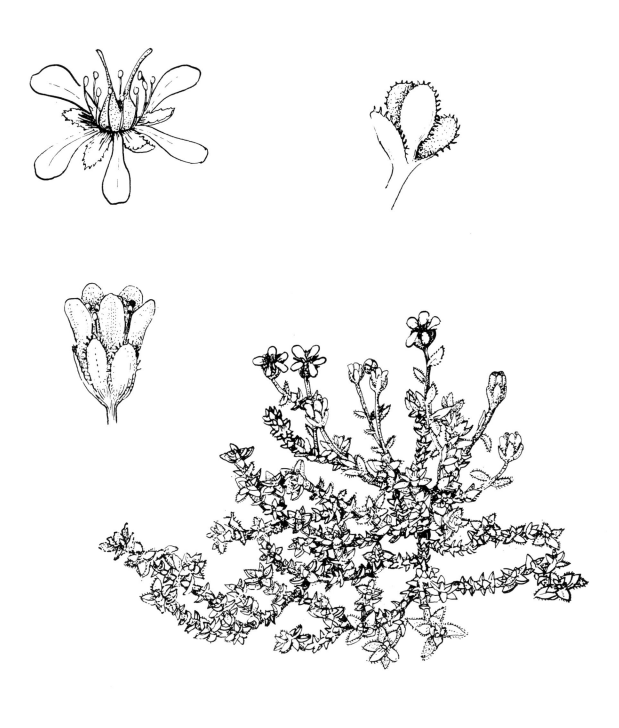

Fig. 73. Purple Mountain Saxifrage *(Saxifraga oppositifolia):*   Habit X1; flowers X5; paired leaves X5.

Saxifraga rivularis L. var. *rivularis* (Alpine Brook Saxifrage). Map 96. Known in New England only from a few wet sites on Mt. Washington, NH. A high arctic species, circumpolar distribution; disjunct to southern Labrador and northwestern Newfoundland, the Gaspé Peninsula, Quebec, and New Hampshire.

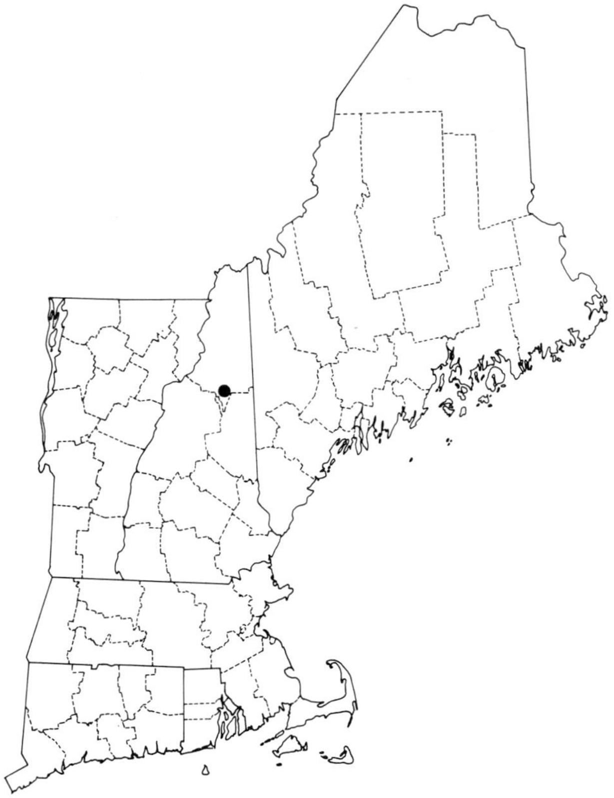

Map 96
Saxifraga rivularis var. *rivularis*

Saxifraga stellaris L. var. *comosa* Poir (Star Saxifrage). Map 97. A disjunct, known only from a few wet sites on Mt. Katahdin, Maine. High arctic regions; amphi-Atlantic distribution, very rare in North America.

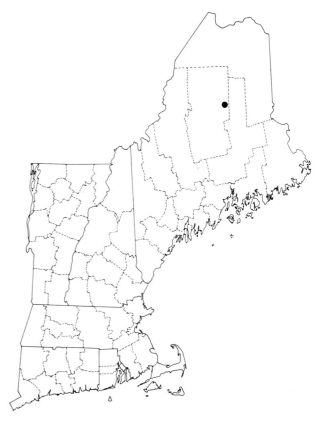

Map 97
Saxifraga stellaris var. *comosa*

SCROPHULARIACEAE (Figwort or Snapdragon Family)

Agalinis neoscotica (Greene) Fern. (Nova Scotian Purple Gerardia). Map 98. Occurring at a single coastal site in northern Maine. Endemic to a small area including Sable Island and western Nova Scotia and the single New England locality in Maine. The taxon is sometimes treated as *A. purpurea* L. var. *neoscotica* (Greene) Gleason; it does not appear on the Nova Scotia list of rare plants.

Euphrasia oakesii Wettst. (Oakes' Eyebright). Fig. 74. Map 99. Stony ground in the alpine of Mt. Washington, New Hampshire and Mt. Katahdin, Maine. Alpine habitats in southern Labrador, Newfoundland, and Quebec; disjunct to Maine and New Hampshire.

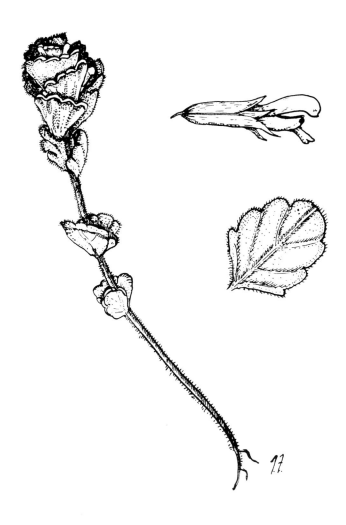

Fig. 74. Oakes' Eyebright *(Euphrasia oakesii)*: Habit X2; flower X6; leaf X2.

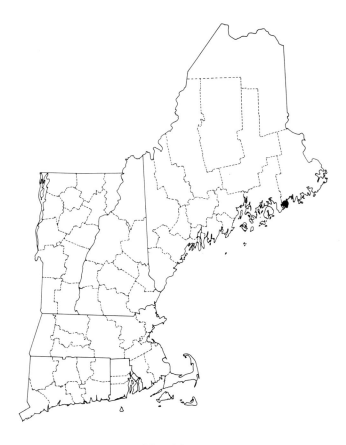

Map 98
Agalinis neoscotica

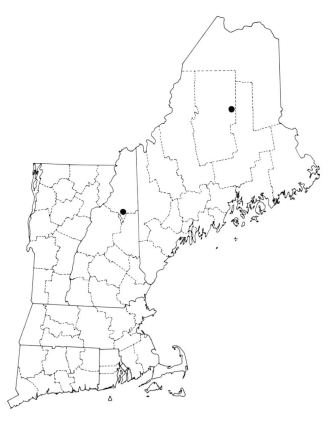

Map 99
Euphrasia oakesii

VIOLACEAE (Violet Family)

Hybanthus concolor (T. F. Forst.) Spreng. (Green Violet). Fig. 75. Map 100. Known in New England from a wooded talus site in western Connecticut. A southern species, ranges from Georgia to Mississippi, Arkansas, and Kansas, north to southern Michigan, southern Ontario, New York, and Connecticut.

Map 100
Hybanthus concolor

Viola labradorica Schrank (Labradoran Violet). Map 101. Russell, in contrast to Fernald, considers this taxon distinct from *V. adunca* var. *minor*. Therefore the New England distribution is still in question. Russell cites only Mt. Washington, New Hampshire, but two Maine specimens belonging to this taxon have recently been confirmed. Ranges from Newfoundland to Alaska; Greenland.

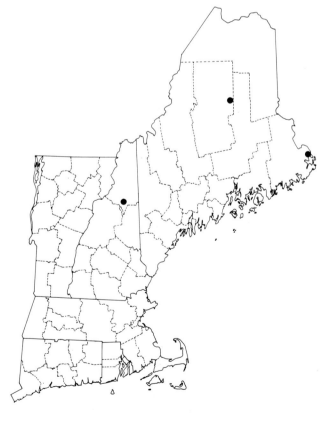

Map 101
Viola labradorica

Fig. 75. Green Violet (*Hybanthus concolor*):   Habit X1; flower X2; petal with shallow notch X5.

REFERENCES

Abbe, E.C. 1948. *Braya* in boreal eastern America. Rhodora 50: 1-15.

Anderson, G. J. 1980. The status of the very rare *Prunus gravesii*. Rhodora 82: 113-129.

Anderson, G. J. 1980a. Change in status for *Prunus gravesii*. Rhodora 82: 375-376.

Argus, G. W. and D. J. White. 1977. The rare vascular plants of Ontario. Syllogeus No. 14.

Ayensu, E. S. 1975. Endangered and threatened orchids of the United States. Amer. Orchid Soc. Bull. 44: 384-394.

Baldwin, W. T. 1884. The orchids of New England. John Wiley and Sons, New York.

Barneby, R.C. 1952. Revision of the North American Species of *Oxytropis* DC. Proc. Calif. Acad. Sci. 27 177-309.

Barneby, R. C. 1964. Atlas of the North American *Astragalus*. Mem. New York Bot. Gard. 13: 1-594, 597-1288.

Böcher, T. W. 1956. Area-limits and isolations of plants in relation to physiography of the southern parts of Greenland. Meddel. Grønland 124: 8, pp 1-40.

Brackley, F. E. 1981. The Orchidaceae of New Hampshire. M.S. Thesis, University of New Hampshire, Durham, NH.

Broome, C. R., J. L. Reveal, A. O . Tucker, and N. H. Dill. 1979. Rare and endangered vascular plant species in Maryland, in cooperation with the U.S. Fish and Wildlife Service [Region 5, Newton Corner, MA].

Canne, J. M. 1979. A light and scanning electron microscope study of seed morphology in *Agalinis* (Scrophulariaceae) and its taxonomic significance. Sys. Bot. 4: 281-296.

Case, F. W. and W. Schwab. 1971. *Isotria medeoloides*, the small whorled pogonia in Michigan. Michigan Bot. 10: 39-43.

Chaudhri, M. N. 1968. A revision of the Paronychiinae. Meded. Bot. Mus. Herb. Rijks Univ. Utrecht no. 285.

Church, G. L. and R. L. Champlin. 1978. Rare and endangered vascular plant species in Rhode Island. The New England Botanical Club in cooperation with the U.S. Fish and Wildlife Service [Region 5, Newton Corner, MA].

Church, G. L. 1980. Plant conservation concerns in Rhode Island. Rhodora 82: 145-149.

Clarkson R. B., D. K. Evans, R. Fortney, W. Grafton, L. Rader. 1981. Rare and endangered vascular plant species in West Virginia, in cooperation with the U.S. Fish and Wildlife Service [Region 5, Newton Corner, MA].

Coddington, J. and K. G. Field. 1978. Rare and endangered vascular plant species in Massachusetts. New England Botanical Club in cooperation with the U.S. Fish and Wildlife Service, Region 5 [Newton Corner, MA].

Cody, W. J. and D. Munro. 1980 The genus *Listera* (Twayblades) in New Brunswick. Canad. Field-Naturalist 94: 443-446.

Cook, P. W. 1959. Discovery of *Arenaria marcescens* in the United States. Rhodora 61: 123-124.

Correll, D. S. 1950. Native orchids of North America north of Mexico. Chronica Botanica, Waltham, MA.

Countryman, W. D. 1972. Guidelines and criteria for the evaluation of natural areas. Natural Areas Criteria Committee of the New England Botanical Club, Inc. Cambridge, MA.

Countryman, W. D. 1978. Rare and endangered vascular plant species in Vermont. The New England Botanical Club in cooperation with the U.S. Fish and Wildlife Service, Region 5 [Newton Corner, MA].

Countryman, W. D. 1980. Vermont's endangered plants and the threats to their survival. Rhodora 82: 163-171.

Countryman, W. D., J. J. Dowhan, and L. E. Morse. 1981. Regional coordination of rare plant information synthesis by the New England Botanical Club. pp 123-131 *in* L. E. Morse and M. S. Henifin, eds. Rare plant conservation: geographical data organization. The New York Botanical Garden, Bronx, NY.

Critical Areas Program. 1981. Rare vascular plants of Maine. State Planning Office, Augusta, ME.

Crow, G. E. and R. E. Graber. 1981.   Survey of hiker activity and mapping of critical habitat of *Potentilla robbinsiana*. Unpublished report prepared for the United States Forest Service White Mountain National Forest and the United States Fish and Wildlife Service Office of Endangered Species.

Crow, G. E. and R. E. Graber. 1981a.   Research indicates hikers threaten endangered alpine plant. Appalachia 47 (5): 7-8. June issue.

Crow, G. E. and I. M. Storks. 1980.   Rare and endangered plants of New Hampshire: a phytogeographic viewpoint. Rhodora 82: 173-189.

Crow, G. E., W. D. Countryman, G. L. Church, L. M. Eastman, C. B. Hellquist, L. J. Mehrhoff, and I. M. Storks. 1981.   Rare and endangered vascular plants in New England. Rhodora 83:259-299.

Daoud, H. S. and R. L. Wilbur.1965.   A revision of the North American species of *Helianthemum* (Cistaceae). Rhodora 67: 63-82, 201-216, 255-312.

Dyer, R. W. 1981.   Furbish Lousewort Recovery Plan. Unpublished technical review draft, U.S. Fish and Wildlife Service, Region 5, Newton Corner, MA.

Eames, E. G., 1926.   *Pogonia affinis* in Maine. Rhodora 28: 31-34.

Eastman, L. M. 1976.   Old and new locales in the Maine flora. Rhodora 78: 152-154.

Eastman, L. M. 1976a.   Long's Bitter Cress *Cardamine Longii* Fern., in Maine and its relevance to the Critical Areas Program. Maine Critical Areas Program Planning Report No. 17, State Planning Office, Augusta, ME.

Eastman, L. M. 1977.   Auricled Twayblade, *Listera auriculata* Wiegand in Maine and its relevance to the Critical Areas Program Maine Critical Area Program Planning Report No. 58. State Planning Office, Augusta, ME.

Eastman. L. M. 1977a.   Small Whorled Pogonia, *Isotria medeoloides* (Pursh) Raf., in Maine and its relevance to the Critical Areas Program. Maine Critical Areas Program Planning Report No. 24. State Planning Office, Augusta, ME.

Eastman, L. M. 1978.   Rare and endangered vascular plant species in Maine. The New England Botanical Club in cooperation with the U.S. Fish and Wildlife Service [Region 5, Newton Corner, MA].

Eastman, L. M. 1980.   The rare and endangered species in Maine. Rhodora 82: 191-192.

Federal Register. 1978.   Determination that various plant taxa are endangered or threatened. FR 43(81): 17910-17916.

Federal Register. 1980.   Determination of *Potentilla robbinsiana* to be an endangered species with critical habitat. FR 45 (182): 61944-61947.

Federal Register. 1980a.   Endangered and threatened plants: proposal to determine "Isotria medeoloides" (Small Whorled Pogonia) to be an Endangered Species. FR 45(178): 59909-59914.

Federal Register. 1980b.   Endangered and threatened plants; proposal to determine *Paronychia argyrocoma* var. *albimontana* (Silverling), to be a threatened species. FR 45(209): 70949-70952.

Federal Register. 1980c.   Endangered and threatened wildlife and plants: review of plant taxa for listing as endangered or threatened species. FR 45(242): 82480-82569.

Fernald, M. L. 1899.   *Oxytropis campestris* in northeastern America. Rhodora 1: 85-89.

Fernald, M. L. 1902.   The northeastern Carices of the section *Hyparrhenae*. Proc. Amer. Acad. Arts 37: 447-495.

Fernald, M. L. 1906.   *Paronychia argyrocoma* and its New England representative. Rhodora 8: 101-104.

Fernald, M. L. 1911.   A new species of *Scirpus* from Massachusetts and New Jersey. Rhodora 13: 4-8.

Fernald, M . L. 1917.   A new *Cardamine* from southern Maine. Rhodora 19: 91-29.

Fernald, M. L. 1919.   I. The unity of the genus *Arenaria*. Rhodora 21: 1-22.

Fernald, M. L. 1928.   *Oxytropis* in northeastern America. Rhodora 30: 137-155.

Fernald, M. L. 1932.　The linear-leaved North American species of *Potamogeton* section *Axillares*. Mem. Amer. Acad. Arts 17: 1-183. (Mem. Gray Herb. No. 3.)

Fernald, M. L. 1937.　Local plants of the inner Coastal Plain of southeastern Virginia. Rhodora 39: 321-366, 379-415, 433-459, 465-491.

Fernald, M. L. 1937a.　*Braya humilis* (C. A. Meyer) Robinson, var. *leiocarpa* (Trautv.), *comb. nov.* Rhodora 39: 276.

Fernald, M. L. 1942.　The seventh century of additions to the flora of Virginia. Part I. Highlights of field-trips in 1941. Rhodora 44: 341-405, 416-452, 457-479.

Fernald, M. L. 1950.　Gray's Manual of Botany. 8th edition. American Book Co., New York.

Fernald, M. L., R. C. Bean, and C. H. Knowlton. 1919.　Plans for 1919 spring field trip of the New England Botanical Club. Rhodora 21: 86-88.

Fernald, M. L. and K. M. Wiegand. 1910.　A summer's botanizing in eastern Maine and western New Brunswick. Rhodora 12: 101-121.

Field, K .G. and J. Coddington. 1980.　Rare plant species in Massachusetts. Rhodora 82: 151-162.

Gleason, H. A. 1952.　The new Britton and Brown illustrated flora of the northeastern United States and adjacent Canada. 3 vols. Hafner, New York.

Graber, R. E. 1980.　The life history and ecology of *Potentilla robbinsiana*. Rhodora 82: 131-140.

Graber, R. E. and G. E. Crow. 1982.　Hiker traffic on and near the habitat of Robbins' cinquefoil, an endangered plant species. N. H. Agric. Exp. Sta. Bull. 522.

Grimes, E. J. 1921.　A new station for *Pogonia affinis*. Rhodora 23: 195-197.

Haynes, R. R. 1974.　A revision of North American *Potamogeton* subsection *Pusilli* (Potamogetonaceae). Rhodora 76: 564-649.

Hellquist, C. B. and G. E. Crow. 1980.　Aquatic vascular plants of New England: Part 1. Zosteraceae, Potamogetonaceae, Zannichelliaceae, Najadaceae. N. H. Agric. Exp. Sta. Bull. 515.

Hinds, H. R. 1978.　Report on field reconnaissance for *Pedicularis furbishiae* and *Carex josselynii* during the summer of 1977. *In* Corps of Engineers, Environmental Impact Statement, Dickey-Lincoln School Lakes Project, Maine. Appendix F Supplement.

House, H. D. 1921.　Nomenclatural notes on certain American plants -- I. Amer. Midl. Nat. 7: 126-135.

Kott, L. S . and R. S. Bobbette. 1980.　*Isoetes eatonii*, a quillwort new for Canada. Canad. Field-Naturalist 94: 163-166.

Levesque, C. M. 1980.　Taxonomic implications of seed morphology of *Arenaria* and *Minuartia* (Caryophyllaceae) utilizing Scanning Electron Microscopy. M. S. thesis, University of New Hampshire, Durham, NH.

Löve, A. and D. Löve. 1965.　Taxonomic remarks on some American alpine plants. Univ. Colorado Stud. Biol. Ser. 17: 1-43.

Löve, A. and D. Löve. 1966.　Cytotaxonomy of the alpine plants of Mount Washington. Univ. Colorado Stud. Biol. Ser. 24: 1-74.

Löve, A., D. Löve, and B. M .Kapoor. 1971.　Cytotaxonomy of a century of Rocky Mountain orophytes. Arctic Alpine Res. 3: 139-165.

Löve, D. 1968.　Nomenclatural notes of Mt. Washington plants. Taxon 17: 89.

Lownes, A. E. 1917.　Further notes on the orchids of the Asquam region. Rhodora 19: 235-236.

Luer, C. A. 1975.　The native orchids of the United States and Canada excluding Florida. The New York Botanical Garden, Bronx, NY.

Macior, L. W. 1978.　The pollination ecology and endemic adaptation of *Pedicularis furbishiae* S. Wats. Bull. Torrey Bot. Club 105: 268-277.

Macior, L. W. 1978a.　Physiological studies on *Pedicularis furbishiae*, Allagash, ME. *In* Corps of Engineers, Environmental Impact Statement, Dickey-Lincoln School Lakes Project, Maine. Appendix F Supplement.

Macior, L. W. 1980. Population ecology of the Furbish Lousewort, *Pedicularis furbishiae* S. Wats. Rhodora 82: 105-111.

Mackenzie, K. K. 1940. North American Cariceae. 2 vols. New York Botanical Garden, NY.

McNeill, J. 1980. The delimitation of *Arenaria* (Caryophyllaceae) and related genera in North America with 11 new combinations in *Minuartia*. Rhodora 82: 495-502.

Mehrhoff, III, L. A. 1980. Reproductive systems in the genus *Isotria* (Orchidaceae). Abstract Bot. Soc. Amer. Misc. Ser. Publ. 158: 72.

Mehrhoff, III, L. A. 1980a. The distribution, status, and ecology of *Isotria medeoloides* (Pursh) Rafinesque (Orchidaceae). Abstract. Bot. Soc. Amer. Misc. Ser. Publ. 158: 72.

Mehrhoff, III, L. A. 1980b. The reproductive biology of the genus *Isotria* (Orchidaceae) and the ecology of *Isotria medeoloides*. M. S. Thesis, University of North Carolina, Chapel Hill, NC.

Mehrhoff, L. J. 1978. Rare and endangered vascular plant species in Connecticut. The New England Botanical Club in cooperation with the U.S. Fish and Wildlife Service [Region 5, Newton Corner, MA].

Mitchell, R. S., J. Sheviak, and J. K. Dean. 1980. Rare and endangered vascular plant species in New York State. The State Botanist's Office, N.Y. State Museum, Albany in cooperation with the U.S. Fish and Wildlife Service [Region 5, Newton Corner, MA].

Morris, F. and E. A. Eames. 1929. Our wild orchids. Charles Scribner's Sons, New York.

Nylander, O. O. 1921. The orchids of northern Maine. The Maine Naturalist Vol. 1. no. 1.

Oakes, W. 1841. Notice of some rare plants of New England, with descriptions of some new species. Hovey's Magazine of Horticulture 7: 178-186.

Pease, A. S. 1917. Notes on the botanical explorations of the White Mountains. Appalachia 14: 157-178.

Pennell, F. W. 1929. *Agalinis* and allies in North America — II. Proc. Acad. Nat. Sci. Philadelphia 81: 111-249.

Pennell, F. W. 1935. The Scrophulariaceae of eastern temperate North America. Acad. Nat. Sci. Philadelphia Monogr. No. 1.

Pfeiffer, N. E. 1922. Monograph of Isoetaceae. Ann. Mo. Bot. Gard. 9: 79-232.

Porsild, A. E. and W. J. Cody. 1980. Vascular plants of continental Northwest Territories, Canada. National Museums of Canada, Ottawa.

Porter, D. M. 1979. Rare and endangered vascular plant species in Virginia. In cooperation with the U.S. Fish and Wildlife Service [Region 5, Newton Corner, MA].

Richards, C. D. 1976. Report on rare and unusual plant species within the Dickey-Lincoln School Lakes Project Area. Corps of Engineers. Unpubl. data. 8 pp.

Richards, C. D. 1978. Report on survey of the St. John River, Maine and some of its major tributaries for Furbish lousewort, *Pedicularis furbishiae* and Josselyn's sedge, *Carex josselynii*. *In* Corps of Engineers, Environmental Impact Statement, Dickey-Lincoln School Lakes Project, Maine. Appendix F Supplement.

Rollins, R. C. 1953. *Braya* in Colorado. Rhodora 55: 109-116.

Russell, N. H. 1965. Violets *(Viola)* of central and eastern United States: an introductory survey. Sida 2: 1-113.

Schuyler, A. E. 1962. A new species of *Scirpus* in the northeastern United States. Rhodora 64: 43-49.

Schuyler, A. E. 1963. Sporadic culm formation in *Scirpus longii*. Bartonia 32: 1-5.

Schuyler, A. E. 1964. A biosystematic study of the *Scirpus cyperinus* complex. Proc. Acad. Nat. Sci. Philadelphia 115: 283-311.

Schuyler, A. E. 1967. A taxonomic revision of North American leafy species of *Scirpus*. Proc. Acad. Nat. Sci. Philadelphia 119: 295-323.

Scoggan, H. J. 1978. The flora of Canada. National Museum of Natural Sciences. Publ. in Botany No. 7(2,3). National Museums of Canada, Ottawa.

Sheviak, C. J. 1974. An introduction of the ecology of the Illinois Orchidaceae. Illinois State Museum Scientific Paper No. 14. Springfield, IL.

Sinnott, E. W. 1912. The pond flora of Cape Cod. Rhodora 14: 25-36.

Small, J. K. 1897. An apparently undescribed species of *Prunus* from Connecticut. Bull. Torrey Bot. Club 24: 44-45.

Snyder, D. B. and V. E. Vivian. 1981. Rare and endangered vascular plant species in New Jersey. Conservation and Environmental Studies Center, Inc. in cooperation with the U.S. Fish and Wildlife Service [Region 5, Newton Corner, MA].

Sorrie, B. A. 1981. Distribution and abundance of *Eupatorium leucolepis* var. *novae-angliae*. Rhodora 83: 449-454.

Stafleu, F. A. *et al.* (eds.) 1978. International code of botanical nomenclature. Regnum Vegetabile 97.

Steele, F. L. 1964. *Potentilla robbinsiana* in the White Mountains of New Hampshire. Rhodora 66: 408-411.

Stewart, W. G. 1978. *Isotria medeoloides*, the smaller whorled pogonia, new to Canada. Rhodora 80: 587-590.

Stirrett, G. M. 1978. Report on investigations of the flora of northern Maine and northern New Brunswick with particular reference to *Pedicularis furbishiae* and other rare plants. *In* Corps of Engineers, Environmental Impact Statement, Dickey-Lincoln School Lakes Project, Maine. Appendix F Supplement.

Stirrett, G. M. 1980. The status of Furbish lousewort, *Pedicularis furbishiae* S. Wats. in Canada and the United States. Unpublished report prepared for the Committee on the Status of Endangered Wildlife in Canada. Canadian Wildlife Service, Ottawa, Ontario.

Storks, I. M. and G. E. Crow. 1978. Rare and endangered vascular plant species in New Hampshire. Prepared by the New England Botanical Club in cooperation with the U.S. Fish and Wildlife Service. [Region 5, Newton Corner, MA].

Storks, I. M. and G. E. Crow. 1979. Endangered, threatened, and rare plants of the White Mountain National Forest, New Hampshire. Prepared for the White Mountain National Forest, United States Forest Service in cooperation with the N. H. Agricultural Experiment Station, University of New Hampshire, Durham, NH.

Taylor, D. 1981. *Potentilla robbinsiana* educational program and hiker survey. Research Department, Appalachian Mountain Club. Unpublished report prepared for the United States Forest Service White Mountain National Forest and the United States Fish and Wildlife Service Office, of Endangered Species.

Torrey, J. and A. Gray. 1840. A flora of North America. Vol 1, Pt. 3.

Tucker, A. O., N. H. Dill, C. R. Broome, C. E. Phillips, and M. J. Maciarello. 1979. Rare and endangered vascular plant species of Delaware. The Society of Natural History of Delaware in cooperation with the U.S. Fish and Wildlife Service [Region 5, Newton Corner, MA].

Wagner, W. H., E. G. Voss, J. H. Beaman, E. A. Bourdo, F. W. Case, J. A. Churchill, and P. W. Thompson. 1977. Endangered, threatened, and rare vascular plants in Michigan. Michigan Bot. 16: 99-110.

Wallace, J. E. 1951. The orchids of Maine. Univ. Maine Bull. 53, no. 12: 1-80.

Whiting, E. M. and P. M. Catling. 1977. Distribution of the auricled twayblade orchid *(Listera auriculata)* in Canada and description of new stations in southern Ontario, Canad. Field-Naturalist 91: 403-406.

Wiegand, K. M. 1899. A revision of the genus *Listera*. Bull. Torrey Bot. Club 26: 157-171.

Wiegman, P. G. 1979. Rare and endangered vascular plant species in Pennsylvania. Western Pennsylvania Conservancy in cooperation with the U.S. Fish and Wildlife Service [Region 5, Newton Corner, MA].

Wofford, B. E. 1981. External seed morphology of *Arenaria* (Caryophyllaceae) of the southeastern United States. Sys. Bot. 6: 126-135.

AVAILABILITY OF NEW ENGLAND STATE REPORTS

Individuals interested in obtaining any or all of the six separate New England State Reports on Rare and Endangered Vascular Plant Species prepared by the New England Botanical Club in cooperation with the U.S. Fish and Wildlife Service should contact the National Technical Information Service (NTIS). Report order numbers and price codes are as follows:

REPORT	ORDER NUMBER	PRICE CODES Paper Copy	Microfiche
New Hampshire	PB 80168933	AO5	AO1
Massachusetts	PB 80176126	AO4	AO1
Rhode Island	PB 80176159	AO2	AO1
Maine	PB 80176167	AO3	AO1
Connecticut	PB 80176175	AO3	AO1
Vermont	PB 81106734	AO4	AO1

The reports can be ordered by writing:

U.S. Department of Commerce
National Technical Information Service
Springfield, VA 22161

Citing the appropriate order numbers and price codes will expedite receipt of reports.

NEW ENGLAND COUNTIES

Aroostook

Piscataquis

Somerset

Penobscot

Franklin

Washington

Hancock

Waldo

Oxford

Kennebec

Knox

Lincoln

Cumberland

Sagadahoc

Androscoggin

Grand Isle

Franklin

Orleans

Essex

Coos

Lamoille

Chittenden

Caledonia

Washington

Addison

Orange

Grafton

Carroll

Rutland

Windsor

York

Belknap

Strafford

Sullivan

Merrimack

Rockingham

Bennington

Windham

Cheshire

Hillsboro

Middlesex

Essex

Berkshire

Franklin

Worcester

Suffolk

Hampshire

Hampden

Norfolk

Plymouth

Litchfield

Hartford

Kent

Barnstable

Fairfield

New Haven

New London

Nantucket

Tolland

Dukes

Bristol, MA

Bristol, RI

Middlesex

Newport

Providence

Washington

Windham

INDEX OF COMMON NAMES

INDEX OF SCIENTIFIC NAMES